Biology
Miller & Levine

From Theory to Practice

Accelerating the Progress of English Language Learners

Strategies for the Biology Classroom

Overview by Dr. Jim Cummins, Program Consultant

Professor and Research Chair, Ontario Institute for Studies in Education

Specializing in research focused on language
and literacy development in multilingual schools

PEARSON

Boston, Massachusetts   Chandler, Arizona   Glenview, Illinois   Upper Saddle River, New Jersey

Contents

Photo Credit: p.1, Jen-Yi Wu

ISBN-13: 978-0-13-368650-0

ISBN-10:   0-13-368650-7

4 5 6 7 8 9 10   V084   14 13 12 11

To the Teacher

Teachers and schools across the United States are welcoming increasing numbers of English language learners (ELLs) into their classrooms. English language learners make up the fastest growing K–12 student population in the United States. In fact, the population of English language learners in U.S. public schools grew by nearly 60 percent from the 1995–1996 school year through 2005–2006 (NCELA, 2008). And, it is expected that this student population will continue to grow over the next several decades (Collier and Thomas, 2002; Leos, 2004).

While English language learners share many characteristics with other students, they need support and scaffolding that are specific to them. Why? Because they represent a highly diverse population. They come from many home language backgrounds and cultures. They have a wide range of prior educational and literary experiences in their home languages. And, they come to school with varying levels of English language proficiency and experience with mainstream U.S. culture.

Clearly, English language learners are an increasingly large and important population of students. Helping these students learn, therefore, is becoming both a necessary and integral part of a typical American classroom.

But helping English language learners acquire content mastery is not enough. English language learners are also expected to participate in yearly high-stakes tests. Research has consistently shown that ELLs usually require at least five years, on average, to catch up to native-speaker norms in academic language proficiency (Cummins, 1981). Nevertheless, many English language learners must take the tests whether or not they have developed academic language proficiency in English.

So, how do you, a biology teacher, help your English language learners clear the hurdles of language acquisition while at the same time ensuring that they attain the same high-level content mastery as your other students? To start, this handbook has been designed to help you identify and respond appropriately to the varying needs of ELLs in your classrooms. It provides insight on how to help ELLs develop fluency as readers, writers, listeners, and speakers of academic English, while learning biology concepts at the same time. In addition, it offers strategies and activities to help you scaffold and support ELL instruction so that all your students can learn in ways that are comprehensible and meaningful, and in ways that promote academic success and achievement.

Whether you have one English language learner in your classroom or many, the strategies and solutions offered in this handbook will hopefully help you feel more prepared to help your English language learners excel both today and in the future.

References

Anthony, A. R. Beckman (2008) "Output strategies for English language learners: Theory to practice." *The Reading Teacher, 61(6)*, 472–482.

August, D., and T. Shanahan, (Eds.). *Developing Literacy in Second-Language Learners: Report of the National Literacy Panel on Language-Minority Children and Youth.* Executive Summary, 2006.

Barrera, R. B., and R. T. Jiménez. *Literacy Instruction for Bilingual Latino Students: Teachers' Experiences and Knowledge.* Office for Bilingual Education and Minority Language Affairs, Washington D.C. 2000.

Beilenberg, B., and Lily Wong Fillmore. "The English They Need for the Test." *Educational Leadership, Vol. 64, No. 4*, December 2004/January 2005.

Collier, V., and Thomas, W. (2002). *A National study of school effectiveness for language minority students' long-term academic achievement.* Santa Cruz, CA, and Washington, DC: Center for Research on Education, Diversity & Excellence. http://www.crede.org/research/llaa/1.1_es/html

Cummins, J. "Affirming Identity in Multilingual Classrooms." *Educational Leadership*, (63)1, 38–43, 2005.

Cummins, J. "A Proposal for Action: Strategies for Recognizing Heritage Language Competence as a Learning Resource within the Mainstream Classroom." *The Modern Language Journal*, 89, 585–592, 2005.

Cummins, J. "BICS and CALP: Clarifying the Distinction." *Working Papers on Bilingualism*, No. 20, 1999.

Cummins, J. (1981). The role of primary language development in promoting educational success for language minority students. In *Schooling and Language Minority Students: A Theoretical Framework.* Sacramento, CA: California Department of Education.

Fillmore, L. Wong. "English Learners and Mathematics Learning: Language Issues to Consider," in *Assessing Mathematical Proficiency*. MSRI Publications, Volume 53, 2007.

Fillmore, L. Wong, and Catherine E. Snow. "What Teachers Need to Know About Language." ERIC Special Report, 2000.

Garcia, Georgia Earnest. "The Literacy Assessment of Second-Language Learners." Center for the Study of Reading, September 1992.

Garcia, G. E. "Supporting Second Language Literacy: Enhancing the English Literacy Development of Students Who Are Learning English-as-a-second-language." *Illinois Reading Council Journal*, 22(1) Special Supplement.

Garcia, Georgia Earnest, and Eurydice Bouchereau Bauer. "Lessons from a Classroom Teacher's Use of Alternative Literacy Assessment." *Research in the Teaching of English*, Volume 36, May 2002.

Garcia, Georgia Earnest, and Heriberto Godina. "Bilingual Preschool Children's Participation in Classroom Literacy Activities: 'Once Upon a Time' and Its Alternatives." *Paper presented at the Annual Meeting of the National Reading Conference*, 1994.

Garcia, Georgia Earnest, and Sarah J. McCarthey. "English Language Learners Writing Practices and Attitudes." *Written Communication*, Vol. 22 No. 1, January 2005.

Garcia, Georgia Earnest, and P. David Pearson. "Modifying Reading Instruction to Maximize Its Effectiveness for All Students." Technical Report #489, Urbana Center for the Study of Reading, Illinois University, 1990.

Jiménez, R. T. "Key Research, Policy, and Practice Issues for fostering the Literacy Development of Latino Students." *Focus on Exceptional Children*, 34(6), 1–10, 2002.

Jiménez, R.T., G. E. Garcia, and P. D. Pearson. "The Reading Strategies of Bilingual Latino/a Students Who Are Successful English Readers: Opportunities and Obstacles." *Reading Research Quarterly*, 31(1), 90–106, 1996.

Kieffer, M. J., and N. K. Lesaux. "Breaking Down Words to Build Meaning: Morphology, Vocabulary, and Reading Comprehension in the Urban Classroom." *The Reading Teacher*, 61, 134–144, 2007.

Leos, K., (2004). *No Child Left Behind.* Paper presented at the annual conference of the National Association for Bilingual Education, Albuquerque, NM.

National Clearinghouse for English Language Acquisition (NCELA). (2008). *Educating English language learners: Building teacher capacity.* Washington, DC. http://www.ncela.gwu.edu/practice/mainstream/volume_I.pdf

National Clearinghouse for English Language Acquisition (NCELA). (2008). *How many school-aged limited English proficient (LEP) students are there in the U.S.?* Washington, DC. http://www.ncela.gwu.edu/expert/faq/01leps.html

National Education Association (NEA). (2008). NEA *2008 Campaign Briefing Book.* Washington, DC. http://educationvotes.nea.org/userfiles/08%20CampaignBriefbk_bw.pdf

NCTE Position Paper on the Role of English Teachers in Educating English Language Learners (ELLs).

Schleppegrell, M. J., M. Achugar, and T. Oteiza. "The grammar of history: Enhancing content-based instruction through a functional focus on language." *TESOL Quarterly*, 38(1), 67–93, 2004.

Short, D., J. Crandall, and D. Christian. *How to Integrate Language and Content Instruction: A Training Manual.* The Center for Applied Linguistics, 1989.

Short, D., and J. Echevarria. "Teacher Skills to Support English Language Learners." *Educational Leadership* 62(4), 2004–5.

Linguistic Ecology
Teaching ELL Students in the Biology Classroom

By Jim Cummins
The University of Toronto

Language and the School Curriculum

Language is central to the teaching of virtually every school subject. The concepts embedded in the curriculum are inseparable from the language we use to teach these concepts to our students. For example, scientific concepts such as *photosynthesis, ecosystem,* and *evolution* are not just ideas that belong in the realm of science; they also belong in the realm of language and are encoded linguistically.

The Challenges of Academic Language

The intersection of language and content entails both challenges and opportunities in teaching English language learners (ELL). It is clearly challenging to teach complex scientific content to students whose knowledge of English academic language may be considerably below the level assumed by the curriculum and textbooks. In a typical biology lesson, for example, several difficult words may be explained in the margins. However, there may be many more words in each lesson that are new to ELL students. These gaps in their knowledge of academic language are likely to seriously impede their understanding of the text.

Students may also be unfamiliar with grammatical constructions and typical conventions of academic writing that are present in the text. For example, academic texts frequently use passive voice, whereas we rarely use this construction in everyday conversation. Also, students are often given writing assignments to demonstrate their understanding. Without strong writing skills in English, ELL students will find it difficult to demonstrate content knowledge.

Obviously, teachers focus their instruction on explaining concepts to students, but ELL students may not yet have acquired the English proficiency to understand explanations that are accessible to native speakers of the language. Thus, a major challenge for teachers is to teach content effectively to *all* students, particularly those who are not yet fully proficient in English. Although this challenge is formidable, particularly at the secondary level, teachers can draw on a knowledge base of recent research findings in order to implement instructional approaches that have proved highly effective in enabling ELL students to gain access to academic content.

Students who are learning science are also learning the language of science.

Opportunities for Extending Language

Content teachers are usually acutely aware of the challenges of teaching ELL students within the subject-matter classroom. However, they may be less aware of the opportunities that exist for extending students' knowledge of academic English. Students who are learning science are also learning the language of science. They are learning, for example, that there are predictable patterns in the ways we form abstract nouns that describe scientific processes. For example, many of these nouns are formed by adding the suffix *-tion* to the verb, as in *fluctuate/fluctuation, evolve/evolution,* etc.

Similarly, when students report back to the class on their observations of a hands-on experience or project, teachers have the opportunity to model the kinds of explicit formal language that is required to talk and write about scientific phenomena. The feedback they provide to students on their oral or written assignments clarifies not only the scientific concepts that students are learning but also the language forms, functions, and conventions that are required to discuss these concepts. Thus, biology teachers are also language teachers and have significant opportunities to extend students' ability to understand and use academic language.

The Knowledge Base

There is considerable agreement among researchers about the general patterns of academic development among ELL students and the factors that support students in catching up academically. The following findings are well-established:

The language of academic success in school is very different from the language we use in everyday conversational interactions. Face-to-face conversational interactions are supported by facial expressions, eye contact, gestures, intonation, and the immediate concrete context. Conversational interactions among native-speakers draw on a core set of high-frequency words (approximately 2000) and use a limited set of grammatical constructions and discourse conventions. Academic language, by contrast, draws on a much larger set of low-frequency words, including both general academic words and the specific technical vocabulary of a particular content area (e.g., *nucleus, habitat,* etc.). This language is found predominantly in two places—classrooms and texts (both printed and electronic).

%

The number of ELLs has grown rapidly in the last 15 years, to about **5 million** students. Estimates project this number will increase 100%, to **10 million,** by 2015 (NEA, 2008).

ELL students typically require at least five years to catch up academically to native speakers; by contrast, basic conversational fluency is usually acquired within 1–2 years. These trajectories reflect both the increased linguistic complexity of academic language and the fact that ELL students are attempting to catch up to a moving target. Students whose first language is English are not standing still waiting for ELL students to catch up. Every year, they make gains in reading, writing, and vocabulary abilities. So, ELL students have to learn faster to bridge the gap. The fact that at least five years is typically required for ELL students to catch up academically highlights the urgency of providing academic and linguistic support to students *across the curriculum.* Ideally, ESL teachers and subject-matter teachers will work together to enable ELL students to develop the academic language skills they need to access subject-matter content and succeed academically.

Sustained growth in reading and writing skills is strongly related to students' level of literacy engagement. If academic language is found predominantly in classrooms and texts, then it is not surprising that active classroom participation and engaged reading of texts across a range of genres is strongly related to the development of academic language proficiency. In the biology classroom, literacy engagement can be interpreted as the extent to which students actively explore biology concepts orally, in writing, and during engaged reading and classroom instruction.

All learning builds on a foundation of preexisting knowledge and skills. For ELL students in the early stages of learning English, this conceptual foundation is likely to be encoded predominantly in their home language (L1). This finding implies that students' L1 is potentially relevant to learning English academic skills and concepts. Students' L1 is the cognitive tool they have used to interact with the world and learn academic content. Thus, rather than ignoring students' L1, we should consider teaching for transfer across languages and encourage students to use their L1 as a stepping stone to higher performance in English academic tasks.

The Pearson ELL Curriculum Framework

The core principles of teaching ELL students across the curriculum are outlined in The Pearson ELL Curriculum Framework. This framework was designed to assist content-area teachers in addressing the needs of ELL students. The five principles in the outer circle of the framework represent the ways in which the teacher plans and organizes the delivery of instruction. The three processes in the inner circle highlight what teachers attempt to do in direct interaction with their students. As depicted in the diagram, these principles and processes flow into each other and represent components or phases of a dynamic whole.

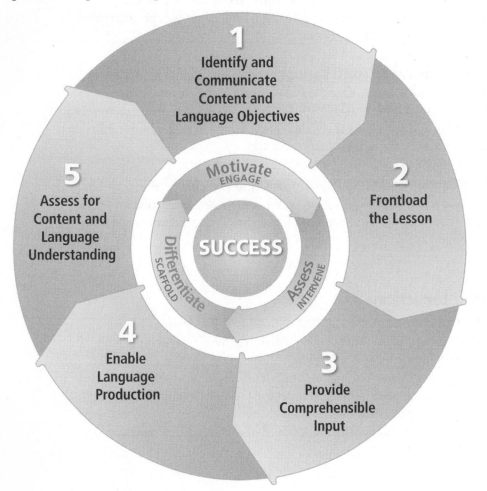

1 **Identify and Communicate Content and Language Objectives**
In planning and organizing a lesson, teachers must first identify what content and language objectives they will attempt to communicate to students. For example, an early focus in a biology course might be on the scope of the field itself—what phenomena are encompassed within the field of biology? These issues might be explored by challenging students to investigate the etymology of the word *biology*. Students will soon discover that the word originates from the Greek words *bios* (meaning "life") and *logos* (meaning "rational discourse"). So, biology is the scientific study of living things. This basic language objective might be extended by asking students to investigate other English words that incorporate the word *bios* (e.g., *autobiography*, etc.).

2 **Frontload the Lesson** Frontloading refers to the use of prereading or preinstructional strategies that prepare English language learners to understand new academic content. It involves strategies such as activating prior knowledge, building background, previewing text, preteaching vocabulary, and making connections.

3 **Provide Comprehensible Input** Language and content that students can understand is referred to as comprehensible input. Teachers make use of nonlinguistic supports to enable students to understand language and content that would otherwise have been beyond their comprehension. Typical supports or "scaffolds" include graphic organizers, photographs, illustrations, models, demonstrations, outlines, etc. Language clarification and use of paraphrasing also contribute to making the input comprehensible.

4 **Enable Language Production** Language production complements comprehensible input and is an essential element in developing expertise in academic language. Use of both oral and written language enables students to solve problems, generate insights, express their ideas and identities, and obtain feedback from teachers and peers.

5 **Assess for Content and Language Understanding** Finally, the instructional cycle flows into assessing what students have learned and then spiraling upwards into further development of students' content knowledge and language expertise.

Classroom Interactions

When we shift into the actual classroom interactions that this lesson cycle generates, a primary focus is on the extent to which teachers' interactions with students motivate them to engage academically. Promotion of motivation and engagement represents a process of negotiating identities between teachers and students. Students who feel their culture and personal identity validated in the classroom are much more likely to engage with academic content than those who perceive that their culture and identity are ignored or devalued. An excellent way of enabling ELL students to take pride in their academic accomplishments is to encourage (or require) them to undertake challenging project work while providing the support to enable them to complete the task successfully.

Differentiation of instruction is widely accepted as necessary to address the learning needs of a diverse school population. One-size-fits-all programs typically exclude ELL students from meaningful participation. When applied to ELL students, differentiation involves scaffolding of input to students and output from students. Activating prior knowledge and building background knowledge is one example of a differentiation/scaffolding strategy.

%

*Of teachers with ELLs, only **29.5%** have been trained to teach English language learners effectively. And, **57%** of teachers think they need additional training to teach ELLs effectively (NCELA, 2008).*

Assessment and intervention are fused into the cycle of motivating students and providing differentiated instruction that addresses the background knowledge and learning needs of individual students. It is essential that teachers regularly assess the extent to which ELL students understand the content presented through classroom instruction and in the textbook. If not, many students who are still in the process of learning academic English may grasp only a fraction of this content. This formative assessment represents an ongoing process in the classroom and, in comparison to most standardized tests, gives the teacher information that is immediately relevant to intervention and further scaffolding of instruction.

Conclusion

The knowledge base that research has generated about ELL students' academic trajectories shows clearly that ELL students must be understanding instruction and learning English across the curriculum if they are to catch up in time to meet graduation requirements. Teaching biology affords opportunities for extending ELL students' academic language proficiency. The Pearson ELL Curriculum Framework incorporates the essential elements that teachers need to implement effective instruction for all students—English-language and native English-speaking learners alike.

Language Proficiency Chart

Use this chart to understand language proficiency levels in the four skill areas of listening, speaking, reading, and writing. Note that an English language learner will not necessarily be at the same proficiency level in all four skill areas.

		Level 1 Low Beginning **Entering/Starting**	Level 2 High Beginning **Beginning/Emerging**
		BEGINNING	
CHARACTERISTICS OF THE ENGLISH LANGUAGE LEARNER	**Listening Skills**	• Minimal comprehension • One-step directions • Comprehends oral facts accompanied by pictures	• Limited comprehension • Two-step directions • Oral descriptions
	Speaking Skills	• Minimal speaking production • Individual words or two- to three-word phrases • Gestures and actions to communicate	• Two- or three-word phrases to some simple sentences • Simple information questions • Simple descriptions
	Reading Skills	• High-frequency words • Slowly, word-by-word • Concrete words represented by pictures • Environmental print • Sound/symbol/word relations • Picture dictionaries and glossaries	• Dependence on visuals and prior knowledge • Multi-step directions • Able to follow text that is being read aloud • Locate specific information • Bilingual dictionaries and glossaries
	Writing Skills	• Little or no ability • Express ideas through pictures and graphics • Label pictures using word bank	• List, label, and copy • Phrases and simple, short sentences • Present tense • Complete graphic organizers • Respond to questions

Level 3 Low Intermediate **Developing**	Level 4 High Intermediate **Expanding**	Level 5 Low Advanced **Bridging**	Level 6 High Advanced **Reaching**
INTERMEDIATE		**ADVANCED**	
• Good comprehension • Simple sentences • Multi-step directions • Oral questions and descriptions	• Very good comprehension • Complex sentences • Understanding and application of oral information	• Comprehension of complex directions and discussions with processing time • Ability to draw conclusions and make connections from oral information	• Comprehension of elaborate directions and discussions • Nearly comparable to native English speakers
• Simple sentences • Simple content-based questions • Description of processes • Retell stories and events • Statement of opinion	• Complex sentences • Discussions of stories, events, and concepts • Speeches and reports • Statement of opinion and defense of point of view	• Nearly proficient • Academic discussions with minimal hesitation • Detailed explanations • Multimedia oral presentations	• Near native ability • Full participation in academic discussions and debates • Effective communication using abstract language
• Use of context clues to determine meaning of words • Sequence pictures, events, processes • Identify main idea • Interpret charts and graphs • Make predictions • English dictionaries and glossaries	• Use of reading strategies • Identify word families • Interpret information • Locate details to support main idea • Match cause to effect • Differentiate between fact and opinion	• A variety of grade-level academic texts with support • Able to use strategies and higher-order comprehension skills with support • Conduct research • Synthesize information from multiple sources	• A variety of grade-level academic texts, nearly comparable to native peers • Application of higher-order comprehension skills with minimal support • Able to critique material and support arguments
• Compound sentences • Paragraphs with main idea and details • Describe events, people, processes, procedures • Give opinions	• Multiple paragraphs • Summarize • Take notes using graphic organizers • Express original ideas • Explain problem-solving strategies • Able to edit/revise	• Expression of ideas at grade level with support • Grasp of basic grammar features • Content-related reports from multiple sources • Multiple genres • Ability to peer edit	• Expression of ideas at grade level with minimal support • Rare grammatical errors • Occasional difficulty for naturalness of phrasing • Grade-level reports • Ability to peer edit with recommendations

Five Essential Principles for Building ELL Lessons

Principle 1 Identify and Communicate Content and Language Objectives

Content Objectives

Effective educational practices, as well as state and federal mandates, require that English language learners meet grade-level standards. The first step in reaching these standards is clearly targeting and communicating the content objectives of a lesson. While the content objectives for English language learners are the same as for mainstream learners, the objectives must be presented in language that suits the students' levels of language proficiency. This involves using simpler sentence structures and vocabulary, paraphrasing, repetition, and avoiding idioms and slang.

Language Objectives

Language objectives focus on promoting English language development while learning content. They can be thought of as a scaffold to help students learn content objectives. Language objectives include: content vocabulary, academic vocabulary, and language form and function.

Content vocabulary These terms are the specialized vocabulary of a subject area. Content vocabulary can be particularly challenging for English language learners who come from a variety of school backgrounds. ELLs should receive explicit instruction of key vocabulary words. Studies show that with this instruction, students are more likely to understand new words encountered during reading.

Academic vocabulary These terms can be described as "school language," or the language that students encounter across all subjects—in discussions, in textbooks, and in tests—as opposed to the informal English words and structures used in conversation. Academic vocabulary includes words such as *summarize, similar, demonstrate, conclude,* and *survey.* Research indicates that acquiring a strong grasp of academic vocabulary is perhaps the most vital factor distinguishing successful students from those who struggle in school. Becoming fluent in academic language will enable English language learners to understand and analyze texts, write clearly about their ideas, and comprehend subject-area material.

Language form and function Language forms include sentence structure and grammar, while language functions involve the purpose of language (such as classifying or comparing). The language forms and functions students need to complete academic tasks should be taught within the context of the lesson. To develop appropriate form and function objectives, teachers can use local and state standards developed for ELLs or coordinate with staff members who specialize in language development. For example, when teaching *greater than/less than,* the language objective might be the structures for comparison (*-er* and *less*) and the function of how to make comparisons.

Teaching Strategies and Support for Principle 1

There are a number of basic strategies teachers can implement to meet the needs of their English language learners. In fact, many are common-sense, everyday strategies that teachers in all content areas already know and use. These strategies lay the foundation for a positive learning relationship between student and teacher.

☐ **Previous lesson objectives** Begin each lesson with a review of the previous lesson's content and language objectives.

☐ **Content objectives** Present the content objectives using visual aids, graphic organizers, and paraphrasing. Write the objectives on the board.

☐ **Prior knowledge** Ask students to talk about the content based on their prior knowledge. Document the results of the discussion with a graphic organizer, such as a KWL chart.

☐ **Content and academic vocabulary** Present content and academic vocabulary.
- Pronounce the word and have students repeat.
- Provide examples, descriptions, visuals, and explanations.
- Clarify the part of speech and discuss cognates, synonyms, and antonyms.
- Ask students to provide examples, descriptions, visuals, and explanations of their own to determine comprehension.

☐ **Vocabulary notebooks** Have students keep a vocabulary notebook. Suggest they use their own words to define the terms and incorporate visuals whenever possible.

☐ **Word-analysis strategies** Teach students word-analysis strategies so that new words can be attacked independently. For example, teach the prefix and the root of a vocabulary word. Write the meaning of the prefix and the root word on the board and have students do the same in their vocabulary notebooks.

☐ **Academic vocabulary practice** Provide flashcards or flashcard frames for key academic vocabulary. Have students use them for paired or independent practice, both during the week and for subsequent reviews. Encourage students to add personal notes and pictures to their flashcards.

☐ **Vocabulary practice** Design writing assignments so that students practice using the new words.

☐ **Language objectives** With the cooperation of an ELL teacher, provide language objectives at different proficiency levels.

☐ **Opportunities for language objectives** If the lesson's content includes idioms, colloquialisms, or slang, use these as opportunities for language objectives.

☐ **Lesson objectives review** End each lesson with a review of the lesson's content and language objectives and a preview of the next lesson's objectives.

1 Identify and Communicate Content and Language Objectives

Applying Principle 1 in *Miller & Levine Biology*

In the Teacher's Edition

Content objectives are listed at the start of each lesson in the Teacher's Edition. Present these objectives before beginning the lesson. If necessary, rewrite them in simpler language and post them on the board.

For specific language objectives, consult your local and/or state ELL language standards.

> **Objectives**
>
> **10.2.1 Describe** the role of chromosomes in cell division.
> **10.2.2 Name** the main events of the cell cycle.
> **10.2.3 Describe** what happens during the four phases of mitosis.
> **10.2.4 Describe** the process of cytokinesis.

In the Student Edition

Content vocabulary words are provided on the first page of each lesson in the Student Edition. The first use of each term is also highlighted in yellow. Academic vocabulary terms are highlighted in gray. They are also accompanied by a Build Vocabulary margin feature that defines each term and provides additional context.

> **BUILD** Vocabulary
>
> **ACADEMIC WORDS** The adjective **adjacent** means "lying near" or "next to." Joints can form only at adjacent bones.
>
> ▶ *Freely Movable Joints* Freely movable joints permit movement in two or more directions. Freely movable joints are grouped according to the shapes of the surfaces of the **adjacent** bones. Several types of freely movable joints are shown in **Figure 32–3.**

Also, throughout the Student Edition, Build Vocabulary features strengthen students' language skills by explaining language forms such as prefixes and word origins.

In Study Workbooks A and B

Content objectives are listed at the start of each lesson in Study Workbooks A and B. If you have provided simplified objectives, have students write these in their Study Workbooks.

For extra support, Lesson Summaries and Chapter Vocabulary Review pages in Study Workbook A provide students with additional review and practice of content vocabulary. In Study Workbook B, every lesson begins with a Build Vocabulary feature that asks students to brainstorm and record ways to remember key vocabulary terms.

On Biology.com

Students can access Vocabulary Flash Cards, Crossword Puzzles, and Match It activities on **Biology.com** to preview, practice, and review lesson vocabulary.

Applying Principle 1 in *Miller & Levine Biology: Foundation Edition*

In the Teacher's Edition

As in the mainstream Teacher's Edition, content objectives in the Foundation Edition are listed at the beginning of each lesson. Present the content objectives and check that students understand each one.

For specific language objectives, consult your local and/or state ELL language standards.

In the Teacher's Edition, Focus on Academic Language boxes appear throughout the lessons. These boxes list academic vocabulary terms as well as terms that students might find difficult. The boxes also offer teaching suggestions to help introduce and reinforce these terms.

> **Focus on Academic Language**
>
> • multicellular • advantag- • well suited for • ideal conditions • adjust
>
> Review with students the meaning of *multicellular* (having many cells). Explain that the prefix *multi-* means *many.*
>
> **Ask** Can you guess what these words mean? *multiplex* (theater with many screens); *multitask* (do many tasks at the same time); *multitalented* (having many talents); *multiple* (many parts).
>
> Write *advantage, well suited for, ideal conditions,* and *adjust* on the board. Pair students and have them find the words in their reading of the paragraph "Advantages." Have them predict the meaning using context clues and explain their reasoning in their notebooks.

In the Student Edition

In the Student Edition, a Build Vocabulary box introduces and defines content vocabulary terms on every page that a term first appears. Within the lesson, the term is highlighted in yellow. Build Vocabulary boxes also support students' form-and-function knowledge by providing background information on the language form of content vocabulary words. For example, the box may explain the origin of the word or discuss the meaning of a word's prefix.

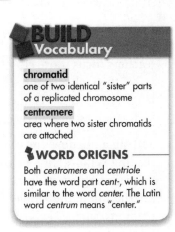

> **BUILD Vocabulary**
>
> **chromatid**
> one of two identical "sister" parts of a replicated chromosome
>
> **centromere**
> area where two sister chromatids are attached
>
> **🖊 WORD ORIGINS**
>
> Both *centromere* and *centriole* have the word part *cent-*, which is similar to the word *center*. The Latin word *centrum* means "center."

In Study Workbook B

Content objectives are listed at the start of each lesson in Study Workbook B. If you have provided simplified objectives, have students write these in their Study Workbooks.

On Biology.com

Students can access Vocabulary Flash Cards, Crossword Puzzles, and Match It activities on **Biology.com** to preview, practice, and review lesson vocabulary.

Principle 2
Frontload the Lesson

Frontloading is the use of prereading strategies that prepare English language learners to read new texts. The goal of frontloading is to reach all ELLs by lessening the cognitive and language loads, thereby allowing them to take control of their learning process.

Frontloading involves the use of the following strategies:

- **Activating prior knowledge:** Instruction is most effective when it links knowledge and experiences students already have to new concepts. Experiences can be academic, cultural, and personal. Teachers can help students see the relationships between their prior knowledge and the new lesson through direct questioning techniques, the use of visuals and graphic organizers, dramatization, and discussion. The more students know about the topic of a lesson, the more they will understand.

- **Building background knowledge:** In order to make a lesson's content accessible to ELLs, teachers may need to familiarize them with social, cultural, or historical facts and concepts of which mainstream learners are already aware. These facts and concepts may be brought out during the activating prior knowledge phase or through direct questioning and instruction.

- **Previewing text:** Previewing text serves the purpose of familiarizing students with what is to come in a lesson and to put them at ease. To preview text, teachers focus more closely on using visual supports such as taking a "picture walk" through a lesson. In addition, English language learners should be taught discrete skills that are required for successfully reading content-area texts, such as how to read and interpret charts, tables, graphs, and maps.

- **Setting a purpose for reading:** Teachers should help students realize that reading is more than reading words and that good readers focus on the message of the text. Teaching ELLs in the content areas also includes explicit instruction in the kinds of text structures they will encounter in content-area readings, such as expository and compare-and-contrast texts. In addition, it includes teaching reading strategies such as identifying the main idea and details, summarizing, and comparing and contrasting.

- **Making connections:** After applying the four previous strategies, teachers can extend the lesson by helping students see relationships between the lesson and other aspects of their lives. For example, connections can be made to other academic subjects, to current events, or to cultural traditions. By incorporating aspects of students' primary language and culture, teachers can ease the transition toward learning the content and language.

Integral to these frontloading strategies is the need for teachers to learn about the backgrounds of the English language learners. Learning about an ELL's experiences validates the student's sense of identity while increasing the teacher's knowledge and broadening the horizons of the English-speaking students in the class. Ignoring the experiences of English language learners puts them at a disadvantage because their backgrounds appear to be irrelevant.

Teaching Strategies and Support for Principle 2

☐ **Prior knowledge** Determine English language learners' prior knowledge of a topic through a variety of activities. For example, have students
- use a KWL chart.
- brainstorm aspects of the topic.
- construct a concept map.
- relate the topic to their personal lives through the use of examples.
- discuss a series of true/false statements.
- put events in a sequence chart or a timeline.
- complete information in a chart.

☐ **Cultural background** Because there may be cultural, historic, or societal factors with which English language learners are unfamiliar, teachers should learn about the background of these students. Teachers can then use this knowledge to determine what additional background knowledge (facts and concepts) need to be presented. For example, before teaching a lesson about stem cells, some students might need an explanation of the role of the U.S. government in regulating and funding scientific research.

☐ **Lesson feature preview** Preview the lesson by calling attention to key features: titles, visuals, captions, charts, bold or italicized words, and any special features.

☐ **Self-questioning strategies** When previewing the text, students should be taught to ask themselves questions such as:
- What do I think this text is about?
- What do I already know about this topic?
- What do the features tell me?
- What kind of reading is it? Narrative? Compare and contrast? etc.

☐ **Predicting strategies** Have students use predicting strategies. They can predict what a text is going to be about by looking at its title and the features. They can also read the first line of a paragraph and predict the theme. Students should always confirm any predictions after reading.

☐ **Notetaking organizers** Present a graphic organizer that students can use for taking notes. Show students how to use headings and subheadings to create an outline framework.

☐ **Set a purpose for reading** Have students set a purpose for reading so they take active control of their learning. After previewing a passage, students should ask themselves questions such as:
- What is this passage about?
- What kind of reading is it? Narrative? Compare and contrast? etc.
- What is my purpose for reading the passage?

☐ **Make connections** At the end of a lesson, have students make a connection between what they have learned with (a) an aspect of their academic lives, and (b) an aspect of their personal lives. This activity can be done as a Think-Pair-Share exercise or in small groups.

2 Frontload the Lesson

Applying Principle 2 in *Miller & Levine Biology*

In the Student Edition

Opportunities for frontloading the lesson are built right into the Student Edition of *Miller & Levine Biology*. The first two pages of every chapter feature an eye-catching photo intended to spark students' interest in chapter content. Use the photo, as well as the Big Idea and Essential Question, to engage students in an introductory discussion of the chapter. Guide them to talk about what they already know, and to think about what they might learn.

The first page of every lesson lists several Key Questions that can be used to preview lesson content. Point out that students can find the answers to the questions by locating key icons and boldface sentences, or Key Concepts, within the lesson.

In the Teacher's Edition

The Teacher's Edition provides several suggestions for frontloading content. Look for either an Activate Prior Knowledge or Build Background activity on the first page of each lesson. These short activities help students start thinking about lesson concepts. Also, each chapter contains at least one Focus on ELL: Build Background box. Use these mid-lesson suggestions to help build ELLs' background knowledge on specific concepts.

To help students make connections, look for "Connect to" notes in the Teacher's Edition. These notes point out opportunities to connect lesson concepts with students' everyday lives (Connect to the Real World) and with other subject areas such as math, health, and social studies.

> **ELL Focus on ELL:**
> **Build Background**
>
> **BEGINNING AND INTERMEDIATE SPEAKERS**
> Refer students to **Figure 11–5,** and have them identify the cell structures they learned about when they studied mitosis. Point out the centrioles, chromosomes, centromeres, and spindles. Use previously learned and new vocabulary terms frequently as you walk them through the visual and ask questions requiring them to use those terms. Then, have students draw and label their own diagrams of the phases of meiosis. Beginning speakers can use single words or phrases or their native language to write captions. Intermediate speakers should write complete sentences. Ask students to describe their diagrams to a partner.

In Study Workbooks A and B

In Study Workbook A, students use a graphic organizer to record what they already know about each lesson before beginning the chapter. At the end of the chapter, they revisit this graphic organizer to record what they've learned. For Study Workbook B, students study a chapter concept map and answer questions about what they expect to learn.

On Biology.com

To preview the lesson, students can use the Lesson Overview on **Biology.com**.

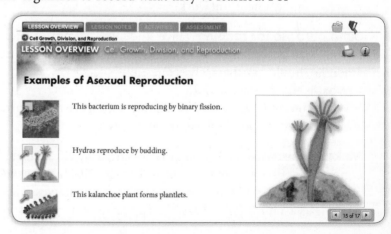

LESSON OVERVIEW · LESSON NOTES · ACTIVITIES · ASSESSMENT

Cell Growth, Division, and Reproduction

LESSON OVERVIEW Cell Growth, Division, and Reproduction

Examples of Asexual Reproduction

This bacterium is reproducing by binary fission.

Hydras reproduce by budding.

This kalanchoe plant forms plantlets.

15 of 17

Applying Principle 2 in *Miller & Levine Biology: Foundation Edition*

In the Student Edition FOUNDATION EDITION

As in the mainstream Student Edition, each chapter opens with an interesting visual, Big Idea, and Essential Question to help generate class discussion on chapter concepts. In the Foundation Edition, the chapter opener also has a Foundations for Learning activity. This activity is a quick way to preview chapter content and vocabulary terms.

Additionally, Key Questions are listed on the first page of each lesson. Use these to preview lesson content. They are then listed again, and answered, at natural stopping points within the lesson.

> **Key Question** What is the job of chromosomes in cell division?
> **Chromosomes make it possible to separate DNA precisely during cell division.**

In the Teacher's Edition FOUNDATION EDITION

Several elements from the first two pages of each chapter help frontload chapter concepts. For example, use the suggestions under Get the Picture to help connect chapter concepts with the introductory visual and activate students' prior knowledge. Also on this page, use the Set the Purpose activity and its accompanying graphic organizer to present students with guiding questions that help them anticipate lesson concepts.

Additionally, every lesson in the Teacher's Edition begins with a list of previewing strategies titled Preview the Pages. Follow the steps in this list to help frontload lesson concepts for students.

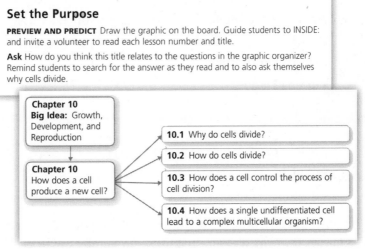

Set the Purpose

PREVIEW AND PREDICT Draw the graphic on the board. Guide students to INSIDE: and invite a volunteer to read each lesson number and title.

Ask How do you think this title relates to the questions in the graphic organizer? Remind students to search for the answer as they read and to also ask themselves why cells divide.

Chapter 10
Big Idea: Growth, Development, and Reproduction

Chapter 10
How does a cell produce a new cell?

10.1 Why do cells divide?

10.2 How do cells divide?

10.3 How does a cell control the process of cell division?

10.4 How does a single undifferentiated cell lead to a complex multicellular organism?

In Study Workbook B

Study Workbook B provides a concept map that helps students preview chapter concepts. They then answer questions about the map and think about what they might expect to learn in the chapter.

On Biology.com

To preview the lesson, students can use the Lesson Overview on **Biology.com**. Have them focus on key words and visuals to help activate prior knowledge.

Principle 3
Provide Comprehensible Input

Providing comprehensible input refers to making written and oral content accessible to English language learners, especially through the use of nonlinguistic supports.

Because English language learners are frequently overwhelmed by extraneous information and large blocks of text, they need help focusing on the most important concepts. With comprehensible input strategies, teachers make information and tasks clear by using step-by-step instructions, by making modifications to their speech, and by clearly defining objectives and expectations of the students.

> Nonlinguistic supports teachers can use to accompany student reading include:
> - photographs
> - illustrations
> - models
> - cartoons
> - graphs, charts, tables
> - graphic organizers, such as flowcharts and KWL charts
> - outlines

Graphic organizers and outlines provide essential visual aids by showing at a glance the hierarchy and relationship of concepts.

> Nonlinguistic supports teachers can use during class presentations include:
> - gestures
> - facial expressions
> - dramatization
> - props
> - tone of voice
> - realia (real-life visuals and objects)
> - models
> - demonstrations

Another effective form of comprehensible input is the "think-aloud," especially as modeled by the teacher. In a think-aloud, the teacher stops periodically and shares how to make sense out of a text or problem by talking about his/her thought processes. The think-aloud shows how thinkers comprehend texts or solve difficult problems. ELLs can practice think-alouds, thereby learning to reflect and comprehend. Teachers can use the student's think-aloud to assess strengths and challenges.

A variety of comprehensible input techniques should be incorporated into lesson plans for English language learners as well as multiple exposures to new terms and concepts. Hands-on activities are particularly helpful to ELLs. The use of multimedia and other technologies will also enhance instruction.

Teaching Strategies and Support for Principle 3

☐ **Visuals** Provide meaningful visuals for English language learners. These may include pictures, images, diagrams, standard graphic organizers (e.g., Venn diagrams, charts, and concept maps), and outlines (filled-in or cloze).

☐ **Multimedia** Use other multimedia to reduce the reliance on language and place the information in a context that is more comprehensible. For example:
- Bring realia (real-life objects) into the lessons. Have visual displays (graphs, charts, photos), objects, visitors, and authentic materials (newspaper and magazine clippings, etc.).
- Use video, audio, and CD/online interactive activities (e.g., Art Review activities on **Biology.com**).

☐ **The five senses** Use teaching techniques that involve the other senses. For example:
- When teaching about plant diversity, have students smell different types of flowers.
- When teaching symmetry, have students trace the outlines of symmetric and asymmetric objects.
- When teaching animal behavior, have students listen to different forms of animal communication.

☐ **Music** Use music as a springboard to some topics. For example, have students listen to and learn the song "Big Yellow Taxi" by Joni Mitchell before a lesson on how humans influence their environment.

☐ **Hands-on learning** Provide hands-on experiences when appropriate to help students contextualize or personalize abstract concepts.

☐ **Demonstrations** Provide demonstrations of how something works, whether it is concrete (such as a water transport in plants) or conceptual (biological magnification of pollutants in organisms).

☐ **Role play** Concepts can also be presented through role play or debates.

☐ **Think-alouds** Use "think-alouds" to model the kinds of question-asking strategies that students should use to construct meaning from text. Write the 5 Ws (Who? What? When? Where? Why?) on a wall chart, and remind students to use these questions as they read to help them understand the text.

☐ **Delivery of instruction** Providing comprehensible input also refers to the delivery of instruction.
- Face students when speaking.
- Speak clearly and slowly. Pause frequently.
- Use gestures, tone of voice, facial expressions, and emphasis as appropriate.
- Avoid the use of idioms and slang.
- Say and write instructions.

3 Provide Comprehensible Input

Applying Principle 3 in *Miller & Levine Biology*

In the Student Edition

Every chapter in the Student Edition of *Miller & Levine Biology* includes numerous images, photos, graphs, charts, and tables that will help English language learners acquire knowledge and skills.

Many lessons include a Visual Analogy or a Visual Summary. These figures are particularly effective for helping ELLs access biology concepts.

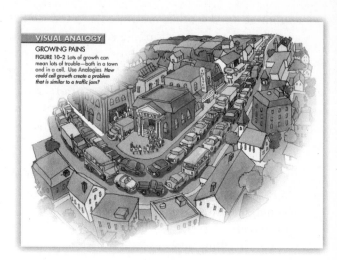

VISUAL ANALOGY
GROWING PAINS
FIGURE 10-2 Lots of growth can mean lots of trouble—both in a town and in a cell. Use Analogies *How could cell growth create a problem that is similar to a traffic jam?*

In the Teacher's Edition

The Teacher's Edition wrap-around provides numerous suggestions for using the comprehensible input that has been built into the Student Edition. For example, Use Visuals notes provide suggestions and questions for working with figures. Visual Analogies are usually accompanied by questions in the wrap-around. And, the English Language Learner differentiated instruction notes often provide guidance for making information more accessible. Pay particular attention to Focus on ELL: Access Content notes.

> **DIFFERENTIATED INSTRUCTION**
>
> **ELL English Language Learners** Model how the organized structure of eukaryotic chromosomes helps cells divide DNA efficiently. Cut 8 long pieces of string (40 cm each) and 8 shorter pieces of string (10 cm each). Combine 4 longer strands and 4 shorter strands in one tangled pile. Then, wind the remaining strands each around an individual pencil. Group this set of pencils and string as a second "genome." Have two volunteers race to divide each of the two genomes in half. Discuss the results of the race.

In Study Workbooks A and B

Study Workbook A includes a graphic organizer activity to be used at the beginning and the end of the chapter. Other graphic organizers within the lessons help students visually organize their thoughts. Students using Study Workbook B study a chapter concept map at the beginning of the chapter and complete graphic organizers throughout the lessons.

On Biology.com

Examples of comprehensible input are found throughout **Biology.com**. For instance, the Visual Analogy features in the Student Edition are further explored on **Biology.com**. Other forms of comprehensible input include Art Reviews and Art in Motion activities. And, the Untamed Science video brings science to life.

Applying Principle 3 in *Miller & Levine Biology: Foundation Edition*

In the Student Edition

As in the mainstream Student Edition of *Miller & Levine Biology*, the Foundation Edition includes numerous photos, illustrations, graphs, charts, and tables that will facilitate English language learners' acquisition of knowledge and skills. In particular, the Build Connections visual analogy features help English language learners more readily access biology concepts by comparing them to real world objects, processes, and concepts.

Also, look for Build Understanding features throughout the text. Many of these features help students organize concepts by using a graphic organizer.

BUILD
Understanding

Venn Diagram Use a Venn diagram to compare and contrast asexual and sexual reproduction.

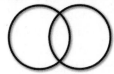

In Your Workbook Go to your workbook to learn more about making a Venn diagram. Complete the Venn diagram started for you.

In the Teacher's Edition

Suggestions for providing comprehensible input to English language learners can be found throughout the Foundation Teacher's Edition. For example, Hands-on Learning activities, which enhance learning for ELLs, are provided for many lessons.

Hands-on Learning

1. Pair students and hand out the materials. **Materials:** two identical rectangular blocks of wood or small cardboard boxes, masking tape, and metric ruler

2. **On the board:** What do you think happens to the surface area when the volume doubles? Have students record the question and their answer in their notebooks.
$a = l \times w = \_\_ \ cm^2$
$v = l \times w \times h = \_\_ \ cm^3$

3. Explain that area units are centimeters squared; for volume, the units are centimeters cubed. Remind students to find the area of each of the six surfaces, then add them together for the total surface area.

4. Tell students the steps. **Step 1:** Calculate and record the volume and surface area of one block or box. **Step 2:** Write a ratio comparing surface area to volume. **Step 3:** Tape the two objects together and repeat Steps 1 and 2. **Step 4:** Evaluate your findings in your notebook.

In Study Workbook B

Study Workbook B includes a chapter concept map at the beginning of the chapter that breaks down the chapter concepts into a simple graphic with uncomplicated terms. Also, activities throughout the lessons are presented with graphic organizers and/or visuals for easy comprehension.

On Biology.com

Activities throughout **Biology.com** provide comprehensible input. These include: Visual Analogy, Art Review, and Art in Motion activities. And, the Untamed Science video brings science to life.

Principle 4
Enable Language Production

Enabling language production for English language learners encompasses the four skills of listening, speaking, reading, and writing.

Because the language used by teachers and in content-area textbooks and assessment is sufficiently different from everyday spoken language, English language learners find themselves at a disadvantage in the classroom. Acquiring academic language in all four skill areas is challenging and requires at least five years of exposure to academic English to catch up with native-speaker norms. Therefore, particular attention should be paid to expanding ELLs' academic language so that they can access the learning materials and achieve success.

While the four language skills are intertwined, English language learners will likely not be at the same proficiency level in all four skills. Teachers will need to modify their instruction in response to students' strengths and needs in each area, keeping in mind the following concepts:

- When providing listening input to ELLs, the language must be understandable and should contain grammatical structures and vocabulary that are just beyond the current level of English language development.

- Teachers should provide appropriate "wait-time" for students to respond to questions. ELLs need time to process the question and formulate an answer.

- For cultural reasons and/or due to lack of oral language skills, ELLs may not express themselves openly or may consider it disrespectful to disagree with authority figures.

- Teachers should encourage students to verbalize their understanding of the content and concepts. Through verbalization, students take responsibility for understanding and explaining their reasoning.

- Think-alouds and recordings of oral reading increase oral language production.

- In addition to frontloading and comprehensible input from the teacher, ELLs need to practice effective reading strategies, such as asking questions, taking notes, predicting, and summarizing.

- There is a direct correlation between speaking and writing; by increasing oral language production, writing skills can be increased. For example, teachers can have ELLs say and write vocabulary to connect oral and written language.

- Writing is usually one of the last language skills in which ELLs develop proficiency.

- Models for writing assignments (such as lab reports) should be presented and discussed. Students should also practice using the model.

- Opportunities for students to write in English in a variety of writing activities should be built into the lessons. For example, reading logs, reading-response logs, and journaling are activities that increase written language production.

Teaching Strategies and Support for Principle 4

☐ **Listening skills** Use audio recordings to develop English language learners' listening skills as well as fluency and accuracy.

☐ **Idioms, colloquialisms, and slang** Give explanations of any idioms, colloquialisms, or slang that arise in content.

☐ **Oral communication activities** Present specific oral communication activities. For example:
- telling or retelling stories
- role playing
- giving instructions
- giving oral reports
- debating
- brainstorming

☐ **Speaking skills** Model summarizing information and reporting on projects or experiences. Then have students summarize and report.

☐ **Reading comprehension skills** Provide explicit teaching of reading comprehension skills. These are particularly important for expository reading. For example, teach or review summarizing, sequencing, inferring, comparing and contrasting, asking questions, drawing conclusions, distinguishing between fact and opinion, or finding main idea and details.

☐ **Reading strategies practice** Have students practice using reading strategies. For example, ask them to
- record the main ideas and details for certain paragraphs.
- develop their own questions.
- write the facts and opinions for certain paragraphs.

☐ **Paraphrase** Provide ELL-appropriate paraphrases of text questions.

☐ **Writing skills** Suggest dialogue journals for note-taking and responses to writing prompts.

☐ **Writing process** Review or teach the steps of the writing process (prewrite/draft/revise/edit/publish).

☐ **Note-taking support** Provide note-taking supports, such as writing templates, fill-in-the-blank guides, or other graphic organizers.

☐ **Self-monitoring** Provide students with checklists for monitoring their own writing, such as checklists for revising, editing, and peer editing.

☐ **Partner writing** Pair ELLs with writing partners for peer feedback.

☐ **Scoring rubrics** Provide scoring rubrics for oral and written assignments and assessments. For example, students' writing can be evaluated for focus, ideas, order, writer's voice, word choice, and sentence structure. Students should be evaluated according to their proficiency levels.

4 Enable Language Production

Applying Principle 4 in *Miller & Levine Biology*

In the Student Edition

Enabling language production consists of practicing listening, speaking, reading, and writing skills. To develop English language learners' listening and speaking skills, use any Student Edition passage. Have ELLs listen to native speakers read aloud and use this listening activity as a model for their own reading. In addition, model asking and answering the Key Questions and figure questions.

The three margin features at the beginning of each lesson support reading skills. First, the Key Questions help students set the purpose for reading. Second, the Vocabulary list preteaches content words students need to know to understand the text. And third, the Taking Notes feature guides students as they read by focusing their attention on important points.

In Your Notebook features, found throughout each chapter, provide frequent opportunities for students to write in English.

 In Your Notebook *Use a cause-and-effect diagram to describe how internal and external regulators work together to control the cell cycle.*

In the Teacher's Edition

The Teacher's Edition notes can be used as a springboard to enable language production. For example, all questions (indicated by **Ask**) are opportunities for listening and speaking practice. These questions can also be used for writing practice. In addition, the Focus on ELL: Extend Language notes have specific suggestions for enabling language production.

> **ELL Focus on ELL:**
> **Extend Language**
>
> **INTERMEDIATE SPEAKERS** To understand the content of this lesson, students need a working knowledge of terms such as *experiment, inferred, concluded,* and *observed.* As students read about the experiments in this lesson, have them locate these terms in the text. Ask students to find a definition for each term in a dictionary and to practice pronouncing each term aloud.

In Study Workbooks A and B

The very nature of a workbook means that Study Workbooks A and B are a primary source for writing opportunities. Many activities in the workbooks also include graphic organizers that will help ELLs organize and improve their writing.

On Biology.com

Instruction that integrates technology enhances ELLs' language production skills. On **Biology.com**, vocabulary words are pronounced for students to repeat. Many of the activities motivate students to improve their reading skills. And the Untamed Science video engages students while improving their listening skills.

Applying Principle 4 in *Miller & Levine Biology: Foundation Edition*

In the Student Edition FOUNDATION EDITION

As with the mainstream Student Edition, use any of the passages from the Foundation Edition to enable English language learners' listening, reading, and speaking skills. Students can listen to native speakers as a model for them to read aloud. In addition, model asking Key Questions. When answering the questions, practice think-alouds.

Margin features found throughout each lesson support reading skills. The Key Questions help students set a purpose for reading. The Build Vocabulary boxes clearly define vocabulary that students need to know to understand the text. And, Build Understanding features guide students as they read by focusing their attention on key points.

In the Teacher's Edition FOUNDATION EDITION

The Foundation Teacher's Edition has been specifically designed to help support both reading instruction and content acquisition. Apply the reading strategies suggested by the Active Reading notes to help enhance English language learners' reading skills. Additionally, all questions (indicated by **Ask**) are opportunities for listening, speaking, and writing practice.

> **Active Reading**
>
> **FIND THE MAIN IDEA** Invite volunteers to take turns reading each paragraph for the 3 phases of Interphase. After each phase is read, stop the read aloud, refer to the diagram, and stress the main idea for that phase as students write them in their notebooks.
>
> **G_1 phase:** The cell increases in size and produces new proteins and organelles.
>
> **S phase:** New DNA is synthesized and chromosomes are replicated, or copied.
>
> **G_2 phase:** Organelles and molecules needed for cell division are produced.

In Study Workbook B

Study Workbook B is a primary source for writing practice. This handbook enhances writing skills through the use of graphic organizers and questions that require written responses.

On Biology.com

Biology.com includes several features and activities that enable language production. For example, vocabulary words are pronounced for students to listen to and repeat. And, the Untamed Science video engages students while improving their listening skills.

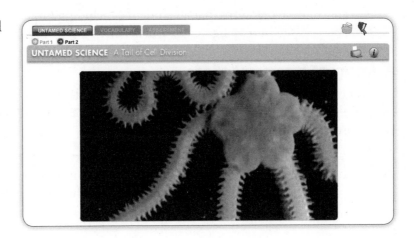

Principle 5 Assess for Content and Language Understanding

An ever-increasing emphasis on assessment requires that all students—including English language learners—achieve the same high standards. Yet below-level language proficiency can have a negative impact on an ELL's success in the content areas. It is, therefore, essential to use assessment results as a way to identify an ELL's strengths and challenges.

Three types of assessments are key to instruction for all students, including ELLs: diagnostic assessment, formative assessment, and summative assessment.

Diagnostic assessment

Diagnostic assessment is used for placing English language learners into the appropriate class, as well as for providing a diagnosis of strengths and challenges.

Formative assessment

Formative assessment is part of the instructional process. It includes ongoing informal and formal assessment, reviews, and classroom observations. Informal assessments include class discussions, teacher observations, self- and peer-assessment, and teacher-student conversations. Formal assessments include essays, quizzes, tests, and presentations.

Formative assessment is used to improve the teaching and learning process—which is particularly important in regards to English language learners. By using formative assessments, teachers can target an ELL's specific problem areas, adapt instruction, and intervene earlier rather than later.

Summative assessment

Summative assessment occurs at the end of a specific period and evaluates student competency and the effectiveness of instruction. Examples are mid-year and final exams, state tests, and national tests.

Federal and state law requires that all students, including English language learners, be assessed in reading, math, and science.

Assessment accommodations

Assessment accommodations for ELLs can minimize the negative impact of language proficiency when assessing in the content areas. These accommodations can be used for formal and informal assessments.

Possible assessment accommodations include: time extensions, use of bilingual dictionaries and glossaries, repeated readings of listening passages, use of dual-language assessments, allowing written responses in the native language, and separate testing locations.

Teaching Strategies and Support for Principle 5

☐ **Informal assessment** Use a variety of informal assessments for ELLs including acting, singing, retelling, demonstrating, and illustrating.

☐ **Content area log** Have students keep a "content area log." Use a two-column format with the headings What I Understand and What I Don't Understand. Follow up with students on the What I Don't Understand items so that they can move those items into the other column.

☐ **Portfolios** Portfolios are a practical way to assess student progress. Provide specific examples of what to include in a portfolio, including examples of speaking and writing. Some portfolio items might be:
- written assignments
- recordings of speaking samples, oral presentations, or role plays
- exercise sheets
- scoring rubrics and written evaluations by the teacher
- tests and quizzes

☐ **Formal assessments** Use a variety of formal assessments such as practice tests, real tests, and oral and written assessments.

☐ **Assessment format** Create tests with a variety of assessment formats, including dictation, multiple choice, cloze, and open-response formats.

☐ **Standardized tests** Have students practice taking standardized tests by using released test items. These are often available online from your state department of education or district website.

☐ **Academic vocabulary** Explicitly teach the academic English words, phrases, and constructions that often appear in standardized test items. This might include *best, both, except,* and *probably.*

☐ **Restate directions** When giving directions, restate the directions in simplified English, repeat the directions, and emphasize key words.

☐ **Repeat directions** Verify a student's understanding of the directions by having the student repeat the directions in his/her own words.

☐ **Bilingual glossaries** Provide students with bilingual glossaries of academic vocabulary.

☐ **Written assessments** Writing portions of assessments are generally the most difficult for English language learners. Therefore, the writing process should be practiced. Teachers should carefully guide students through the prewriting step with examples of brainstorming, outlining, using a graphic organizer, etc.

5 Assess for Content and Language Understanding

Applying Principle 5 in *Miller & Levine Biology*

In the Student Edition

Formative assessment, which includes ongoing informal and formal assessments, is especially important for English language learners. In the Student Edition, the end-of-lesson Assessment is one example of a formal formative assessment. To target problem areas an ELL might have, use the Key Questions as a basis for informal comprehension checks. Use In Your Notebook assignments and figure questions for additional informal assessment opportunities. The chapter-level Study Guide provides a valuable check before the summative chapter Assessment and Standardized Test Prep.

In the Teacher's Edition

The Teacher's Edition includes suggestions that address both informal and formal assessment. The Check for Understanding and Assess and Remediate features include assessment suggestions and tips for adjusting instruction if students are struggling. Use Lead a Discussion notes and questions in the Teacher's Edition wrap-around to assess an ELL's language proficiency. Performance Tasks at the end of each chapter provide summative assessment tasks.

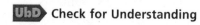

UbD Check for Understanding

ORAL QUESTIONING

Use the following prompts to gauge students' understanding of lesson concepts.

- How does the growth of a tumor relate to normal cell growth and division?
- How does cancer relate to the Big Idea of Growth, Development, and Reproduction?
- What details from this lesson, and past lessons, could you add to the captions of **Figure 10–16** that further explain what is happening in each picture?

ADJUST INSTRUCTION

Help students make the connection between regulation and cancer by asking them to think about what might happen if different real-world controls, such as traffic signals, no longer worked. Reinforce that cancer is the result of uncontrolled cell division.

In Study Workbook B

Study Workbook B contains Chapter Reviews and Standardized Test Prep pages to help students practice taking tests.

On Biology.com

Several features on **Biology.com** will help an ELL be successful in formative and summative assessments. For example, Lesson Overviews, interactive Vocabulary Reviews, and Self-Tests will help target areas in which an English language learner needs remediation.

In the Assessment Resources Book

The tests in the Assessment Resources Book are available online. Edit these tests as necessary to accommodate ELLs at different language proficiency levels.

Applying Principle 5 in *Miller & Levine Biology: Foundation Edition*

In the Student Edition FOUNDATION EDITION

The Foundation Edition of *Miller & Levine Biology* includes built-in opportunities for assessment that are particularly appropriate for ELLs. For example, the Key Question is revisited, along with an answer, at the end of each section in a lesson. Ask students to provide the answer in their own words and then check it against the text. The end-of-lesson Check Understanding boxes provide a formal checkpoint before proceeding to the next lesson. And, the chapter Check Understanding and Standardized Test Prep pages are summative chapter-level assessments.

In the Teacher's Edition FOUNDATION EDITION

The Teacher's Edition includes both informal and formal assessments. A key feature is the Speed Bump. Use Speed Bumps to check that small problems in student content comprehension don't become bigger problems. Use the Wrap Up Activities at the end of each lesson to assess an ELL's language proficiency as well as their understanding of lesson concepts.

> **Speed Bump**
>
> **Ask** What could go wrong if the cell cycle is not carefully regulated? *(DNA may not be divided evenly among the cells. Cells could divide when organisms don't need new cells.)*
>
> Have students draw a Venn diagram in their notebooks to compare internal and external regulators.

In Study Workbook B

Study Workbook B includes a Chapter Summary at the beginning of the chapter and a Chapter Review at the end that can form the basis for assessment of ELLs. Study Workbook B also contains Standardized Test Prep pages to help students practice taking tests.

On Biology.com

Lesson Overviews and Vocabulary Flash Cards on **Biology.com** help students identify problem areas and terms they are struggling to understand. This extra practice and support may help ELLs be more prepared for success on formative and summative assessments.

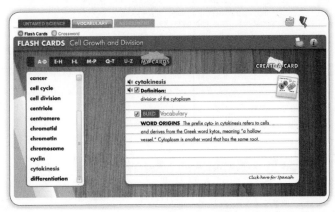

In the Assessment Resources Book

The tests in the Assessment Resources Book are available online. Edit these tests as necessary to accommodate ELLs at different language proficiency levels.

Teaching ELLs With
Miller & Levine Biology

This short how-to guide will help you start looking at the text in a new way—with an eye for the needs of your English language learners. In fact, many of the features in *Miller & Levine Biology* are directly applicable to one or more of the Five Principles for Building ELL Lessons.

Follow the guide as it walks you through a typical lesson, pointing out both the built-in ELL scaffolds and places in the text where your ELLs might need extra support. Use the *On this page . . .* notes to see exactly how the principles can be applied to biology content.

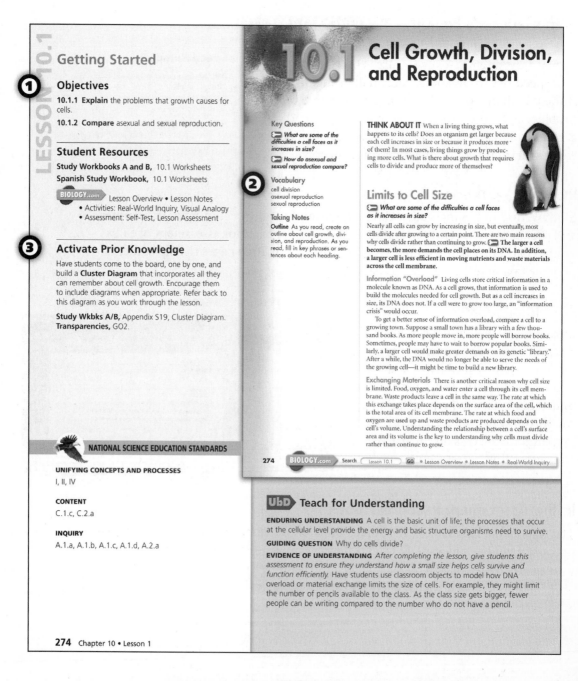

LESSON 10.1

Getting Started

① Objectives

10.1.1 Explain the problems that growth causes for cells.

10.1.2 Compare asexual and sexual reproduction.

Student Resources

Study Workbooks A and B, 10.1 Worksheets
Spanish Study Workbook, 10.1 Worksheets

BIOLOGY.com Lesson Overview • Lesson Notes
• Activities: Real-World Inquiry, Visual Analogy
• Assessment: Self-Test, Lesson Assessment

③ Activate Prior Knowledge

Have students come to the board, one by one, and build a **Cluster Diagram** that incorporates all they can remember about cell growth. Encourage them to include diagrams when appropriate. Refer back to this diagram as you work through the lesson.

Study Wkbks A/B, Appendix S19, Cluster Diagram. **Transparencies,** GO2.

NATIONAL SCIENCE EDUCATION STANDARDS

UNIFYING CONCEPTS AND PROCESSES
I, II, IV

CONTENT
C.1.c, C.2.a

INQUIRY
A.1.a, A.1.b, A.1.c, A.1.d, A.2.a

274 Chapter 10 • Lesson 1

10.1 Cell Growth, Division, and Reproduction

Key Questions

❓ What are some of the difficulties a cell faces as it increases in size?

❓ How do asexual and sexual reproduction compare?

② Vocabulary
cell division
asexual reproduction
sexual reproduction

Taking Notes

Outline As you read, create an outline about cell growth, division, and reproduction. As you read, fill in key phrases or sentences about each heading.

THINK ABOUT IT When a living thing grows, what happens to its cells? Does an organism get larger because each cell increases in size or because it produces more of them? In most cases, living things grow by producing more cells. What is there about growth that requires cells to divide and produce more of themselves?

Limits to Cell Size

❓ What are some of the difficulties a cell faces as it increases in size?

Nearly all cells can grow by increasing in size, but eventually, most cells divide after growing to a certain point. There are two main reasons why cells divide rather than continuing to grow. ❓ **The larger a cell becomes, the more demands the cell places on its DNA. In addition, a larger cell is less efficient in moving nutrients and waste materials across the cell membrane.**

Information "Overload" Living cells store critical information in a molecule known as DNA. As a cell grows, that information is used to build the molecules needed for cell growth. But as a cell increases in size, its DNA does not. If a cell were to grow too large, an "information crisis" would occur.

To get a better sense of information overload, compare a cell to a growing town. Suppose a small town has a library with a few thousand books. As more people move in, more people will borrow books. Sometimes, people may have to wait to borrow popular books. Similarly, a larger cell would make greater demands on its genetic "library." After a while, the DNA would no longer be able to serve the needs of the growing cell—it might be time to build a new library.

Exchanging Materials There is another critical reason why cell size is limited. Food, oxygen, and water enter a cell through its cell membrane. Waste products leave a cell in the same way. The rate at which this exchange takes place depends on the surface area of the cell, which is the total area of its cell membrane. The rate at which food and oxygen are used up and waste products are produced depends on the cell's volume. Understanding the relationship between a cell's surface area and its volume is the key to understanding why cells must divide rather than continue to grow.

274 **BIOLOGY.com** Search (Lesson 10.1) GO • Lesson Overview • Lesson Notes • Real-World Inquiry

---

UbD ▶ **Teach for Understanding**

ENDURING UNDERSTANDING A cell is the basic unit of life; the processes that occur at the cellular level provide the energy and basic structure organisms need to survive.

GUIDING QUESTION Why do cells divide?

EVIDENCE OF UNDERSTANDING *After completing the lesson, give students this assessment to ensure they understand how a small size helps cells survive and function efficiently. Have students use classroom objects to model how DNA overload or material exchange limits the size of cells. For example, they might limit the number of pencils available to the class. As the class size gets bigger, fewer people can be writing compared to the number who do not have a pencil.*

① Content Objectives *(Principle 1)*

- Use the content objectives to preview lesson concepts.

- If needed, rewrite them on the board in simpler language.

- Lesson objectives are also listed in *Study Workbooks A* and *B*.

On this page . . .

- Read objectives 10.1.1 and 10.1.2 aloud. Make sure ELLs understand the meaning of the academic vocabulary terms *explain* and *compare*.

- Have students think about each objective and predict what they will learn in the lesson.

② Content Vocabulary *(Principle 1)*

- Use the vocabulary list on the first page of each lesson to introduce content vocabulary terms.

- If desired, provide students with additional vocabulary practice and support. For example, use the Vocabulary Flash Cards on **Biology.com** or one of the Vocabulary Support strategies listed later in this handbook in Teaching Strategies for English Language Learners.

On this page . . .

- Read aloud the terms: *cell division, asexual reproduction,* and *sexual reproduction.* Have students pronounce each.

- Discuss the terms as a class and have students settle on a definition for each term. Start a word wall for the chapter by posting the terms along with their student-generated definitions.

③ Activate Prior Knowledge *(Principle 2)*

- Look for either an Activate Prior Knowledge or Build Background activity at the beginning of each lesson in the Teacher's Edition wrap-around.

- Use these activities to help introduce the lesson and frontload content for ELLs.

On this page . . .

- Write the term *Cell Growth* in the center of the board and circle it. Call on students to add to the cluster diagram.

- Encourage beginning speakers to add drawings to the diagram.

(1) Difficult Terms *(Principles 1 and 4)*

- Scan the Student Edition for terms that may be difficult for your English language learners.

- Provide language support for these terms. For example, write them on the board and discuss the meaning of each term.

On this page . . .

- Add the terms *surface area* and *volume* to your word wall. Have students write the terms and a quick definition for each in their notebooks.

- Encourage ELLs to write down any other words they struggle with. Define these terms as needed.

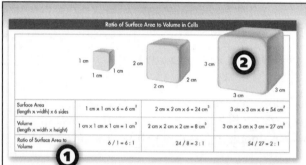

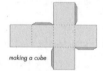

Ratio of Surface Area to Volume in Cells

Surface Area (length × width) × 6 sides	1 cm × 1 cm × 6 = 6 cm²	2 cm × 2 cm × 6 = 24 cm²	3 cm × 3 cm × 6 = 54 cm²
Volume (length × width × height)	1 cm × 1 cm × 1 = 1 cm³	2 cm × 2 cm × 2 = 8 cm³	3 cm × 3 cm × 3 = 27 cm³
Ratio of Surface Area to Volume	6 / 1 = 6 : 1	24 / 8 = 3 : 1	54 / 27 = 2 : 1

► **Ratio of Surface Area to Volume** Imagine a cell that is shaped like a cube, like those shown in **Figure 10–1**. The formula for area ($l \times w$) is used to calculate the surface area. The formula for volume ($l \times w \times h$) is used to calculate the amount of space inside. By using a ratio of surface area to volume, you can see how the size of the cell's surface area grows compared to its volume.

Notice that for a cell with sides that measure 1 cm in length, the ratio of surface area to volume is 6/1 or 6 : 1. Increase the length of the cell's sides to 2 cm, and the ratio becomes 24/8 or 3 : 1. What if the length triples? The ratio of surface area to volume becomes 54/27 or 2 : 1. Notice that the surface area is not increasing as fast as the volume increases. For a growing cell, a decrease in the relative amount of cell membrane available creates serious problems.

FIGURE 10–1 Ratio of Surface Area to Volume As the length of the sides increases, the volume increases more than the surface area. Interpret Tables *What are the ratios comparing?*

making a cube

(3) Quick Lab OPEN-ENDED INQUIRY

Modeling the Relationship Between Surface Area and Volume

❶ Use drawing or grid paper to make patterns for a 6-cm cube, a 5-cm cube, a 4-cm cube, and a 3-cm cube.

❷ Cut out your patterns and fold them. Then use the tabs to tape or glue the sides together. Don't tape down the top side.

❸ Construct a data table to compare the volume, the surface area, and the ratio of surface area to volume of each cube.

❹ Use your data to calculate the number of 3-cm cubes that would fit in the same volume as the 6-cm cube. Also calculate the total surface area for the smaller cubes. **MATH**

Analyze and Conclude
1. Review Describe the function of a cell membrane and its relationship to what happens inside a cell?
2. Apply Concepts How does the surface area change when a large cell divides into smaller cells that have the same total volume?

Cell Growth and Division **275**

Quick Lab

PURPOSE Students will explore the ratio of surface area to volume in different-sized cubes that fill an equal volume.

MATERIALS 1-cm grid paper, tape, scissors

PLANNING Suggest students choose side lengths that are multiples of one another and make enough small cubes to fill the larger cube.

ANALYZE AND CONCLUDE
1. The cell membrane provides the surface across which materials can be exchanged between a cell and its environment.
2. A growing cell requires more surface area because it carries out more activity than a smaller cell. A cell's volume cannot become so large that its cell membrane can no longer bring in enough nutrients or get rid of wastes.

Teach

Build Math Skills

Some students may have limited experience with ratios. Explain that a ratio is a comparison. In this case, it compares the amount of surface area a cell has to its volume. A ratio can be expressed as a proportion, such as 2:1, or as a fraction, such as $\frac{4}{2}$. In **Figure 10–1**, the ratios have been reduced to their simplest form to make it more obvious how the cube's surface area grows in relationship to its volume.

Ask What is the ratio of vowels to consonants in the alphabet? *(5:21 or $\frac{5}{21}$)*

DIFFERENTIATED INSTRUCTION

L1 Special Needs Use clay models to help students understand that a smaller surface area to volume ratio does not mean the cube is getting smaller. Both surface area and cube volume increase as the length of the side increases.

L1 Struggling Students Some students may have a difficult time understanding the information presented in the table. Point out that the cube directly above each column shows the "cell" that the calculations refer to. Then, explain that the first row shows how to find the surface area for each cubic "cell." Use a clay or plastic model of a cube to explain that, when students multiply length and width ($l \times w$), they are finding the surface area of one face of the cube. They need to multiply this area by six, because the cube has six faces.

Answers

FIGURE 10–1 the amount of surface area a cell has to its volume

Cell Growth and Division **275**

---

② Visual Support *(Principle 3)*

- Use Student Edition visuals to scaffold and support student understanding of lesson concepts.

- Walk through the diagrams with your class to ensure ELLs understand how the figure demonstrates lesson concepts.

On this page . . .

- Refer to the cell drawings in Figure 10–1. Point out that the sides of each cubic "cell" make up its surface area, while the space inside the "cell" makes up its volume. Hold up a cube so ELLs can see a physical model of surface area and volume.

- Have pairs of ELLs identify another classroom object and describe its surface area and volume to each other. Pair beginning and intermediate speakers with advanced or native English speakers.

③ Hands-On Learning *(Principle 3)*

- Use Quick Lab and Analyzing Data features to give ELLs hands-on opportunities to explore chapter content.

- Look for Quick Labs that have an accompanying Inquiry Into Scientific Thinking page in *Study Workbook B*. These workbook pages provide modified, accessible activities that are based on existing Quick Labs.

On this page . . .

- Have students perform the Quick Lab on this page. If necessary, discuss each of the four steps as a class to ensure that English language learners understand the procedure.

- Pair beginning and intermediate speakers and have them work through the Analyze and Conclude questions orally before writing answers down. Accept drawings or short phrases as answers from beginning speakers.

- If desired, assign your ELLs the corresponding Inquiry Into Scientific Thinking activity in *Study Workbook B* as an alternate exploration of surface area and volume.

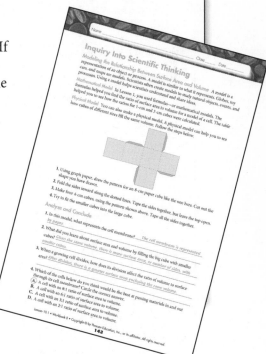

Teaching With The Principles

① Cultural Context *(Principle 2)*

- Look for content that assumes students are familiar with American culture. Provide your non-native students with the background knowledge they need to understand the content.

On this page . . .

- The visual assumes students know the typical structure of American cities. If needed, explain that most U.S. cities have a library, fire station, and so on.

- Encourage non-native ELLs to explain or draw the typical community structure in their native countries.

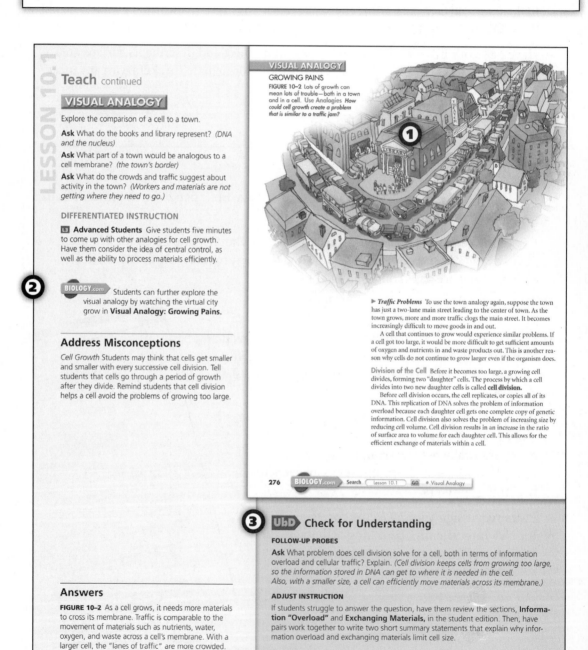

LESSON 10.1

Teach continued

VISUAL ANALOGY

Explore the comparison of a cell to a town.

Ask What do the books and library represent? *(DNA and the nucleus)*

Ask What part of a town would be analogous to a cell membrane? *(the town's border)*

Ask What do the crowds and traffic suggest about activity in the town? *(Workers and materials are not getting where they need to go.)*

DIFFERENTIATED INSTRUCTION

L3 Advanced Students Give students five minutes to come up with other analogies for cell growth. Have them consider the idea of central control, as well as the ability to process materials efficiently.

② **BIOLOGY.com** Students can further explore the visual analogy by watching the virtual city grow in **Visual Analogy: Growing Pains.**

Address Misconceptions

Cell Growth Students may think that cells get smaller and smaller with every successive cell division. Tell students that cells go through a period of growth after they divide. Remind students that cell division helps a cell avoid the problems of growing too large.

Answers

FIGURE 10–2 As a cell grows, it needs more materials to cross its membrane. Traffic is comparable to the movement of materials such as nutrients, water, oxygen, and waste across a cell's membrane. With a larger cell, the "lanes of traffic" are more crowded.

276 Chapter 10 • Lesson 1

VISUAL ANALOGY

GROWING PAINS

FIGURE 10–2 Lots of growth can mean lots of trouble—both in a town and in a cell. Use Analogies *How could cell growth create a problem that is similar to a traffic jam?*

▶ *Traffic Problems* To use the town analogy again, suppose the town has just a two-lane main street leading to the center of town. As the town grows, more and more traffic clogs the main street. It becomes increasingly difficult to move goods in and out.

A cell that continues to grow would experience similar problems. If a cell got too large, it would be more difficult to get sufficient amounts of oxygen and nutrients in and waste products out. This is another reason why cells do not continue to grow larger even if the organism does.

Division of the Cell Before it becomes too large, a growing cell divides, forming two "daughter" cells. The process by which a cell divides into two new daughter cells is called **cell division.**

Before cell division occurs, the cell replicates, or copies all of its DNA. This replication of DNA solves the problem of information overload because each daughter cell gets one complete copy of genetic information. Cell division also solves the problem of increasing size by reducing cell volume. Cell division results in an increase in the ratio of surface area to volume for each daughter cell. This allows for the efficient exchange of materials within a cell.

276 **BIOLOGY.com** Search (Lesson 10.1) GO • Visual Analogy

③ UbD Check for Understanding

FOLLOW-UP PROBES

Ask What problem does cell division solve for a cell, both in terms of information overload and cellular traffic? Explain. *(Cell division keeps cells from growing too large, so the information stored in DNA can get to where it is needed in the cell. Also, with a smaller size, a cell can efficiently move materials across its membrane.)*

ADJUST INSTRUCTION

If students struggle to answer the question, have them review the sections, **Information "Overload"** and **Exchanging Materials,** in the student edition. Then, have pairs work together to write two short summary statements that explain why information overload and exchanging materials limit cell size.

2 **Digital Support** *(Principle 3)*

- Look for **Biology.com** activities that provide ELLs with extra visual support and alternate ways to access content.

On this page . . .

- Use the Student Edition to present the visual analogy to your class. Make sure English language learners understand the basic premise of the analogy: the library is analogous to a cell nucleus, while traffic is analogous to the exchange of materials in a cell.

- Suggest students log on to **Biology.com** and complete the Visual Analogy: Growing Pains activity. Consider pairing beginning speakers with more-proficient speakers to work through the online activity and questions together.

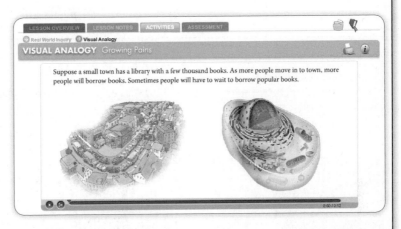

3 **Informal Assessment** *(Principle 5)*

- Frequently check your English language learners' comprehension of lesson concepts.

- Caption questions help you quickly gauge student understanding of figures and how these figures relate to the lesson.

- Check for Understanding boxes provide more comprehensive mid-lesson informal assessments. If your ELLs are struggling, adjust your instruction accordingly.

On this page . . .

- Duscuss the Figure 10–2 caption question as a class. Make sure ELLs understand what the question is asking. Check their answers to ensure content comprehension.

- Write the Check for Understanding question on the board and read it aloud for English language learners. Encourage ELLs to write a response to the question. Accept drawings, relevant terms, or short phrases from beginning speakers.

① **Enable Language Production**
(Principles 1 and 4)

- Look for Build Vocabulary features in the Student Edition.

- Have your students read through and discuss these margin notes to build their knowledge of English language form and function.

On this page . . .

- Point out the Build Vocabulary note to your students. Discuss what a prefix is and how prefixes can affect the meaning of English words. Use the term *asexual* as an example.

- Suggest ELLs brainstorm other words that have a prefix and discuss how the prefix affects the words' meanings.

Cell Division and Reproduction

How do asexual and sexual reproduction compare?

Reproduction, the formation of new individuals, is one of the most important characteristics of living things. For an organism composed of just one cell, cell division can serve as a perfectly good form of reproduction. You don't have to meet someone else, conduct a courtship, or deal with rivals. All you have to do is to divide, and *presto*—there are two of you!

Bacterium
(TEM 32,800×)

FIGURE 10–3 Asexual Reproduction Cell division leads to reproduction in single-celled organisms and some multicellular organisms. **Apply Concepts** *What do the offspring of each of these organisms have in common?*

Hydra
(LM 25×)

Kalanchoe

② **Asexual Reproduction** For many single-celled organisms, such as the bacterium in **Figure 10–3**, cell division is the only form of reproduction. The process can be relatively simple, efficient, and effective, enabling populations to increase in number very quickly. In most cases, the two cells produced by cell division are genetically identical to the cell that produced them. This kind of reproduction is called **asexual reproduction.** ⮞ **The production of genetically identical offspring from a single parent is known as asexual reproduction.**

Asexual reproduction also occurs in many multicellular organisms. The small bud growing off the hydra will eventually break off and become an independent organism, an example of asexual reproduction in an animal. Each of the small shoots or plantlets on the tip of the kalanchoe leaf may also grow into a new plant.

Sexual Reproduction Unlike asexual reproduction, where cells separate to form a new individual, **sexual reproduction** involves the fusion of two cells. In sexual reproduction, offspring are produced by the fusion of special reproductive cells formed by each of two parents. ⮞ **Offspring produced by sexual reproduction inherit some of their genetic information from each parent.** Most animals and plants reproduce sexually, and so do many single-celled organisms. You will learn more about the form of cell division that produces reproductive cells in Chapter 11.

In Your Notebook *Use a Venn diagram to compare asexual and sexual reproduction.*

① **BUILD Vocabulary**

PREFIXES The prefix *a-* in *asexual* means "without." **Asexual reproduction** is reproduction without the fusion of reproductive cells.

Cell Growth and Division **277**

Lead a Discussion

Talk about how cell division relates to the process of asexual reproduction. To reinforce students' knowledge, have them apply what they have learned to their everyday lives.

Ask Why do bacterial infections spread so quickly through a school? *(Bacteria can reproduce asexually. So, they can quickly reproduce in the right environment, such as a crowded school.)*

③ **DIFFERENTIATED INSTRUCTION**

LPR Less Proficient Readers List the Key Concepts on the board in simplified language. For example, write:

- Offspring of asexual reproduction have the same genetic information.

- Offspring of sexual reproduction have genetic information from both parents.

Suggest that students preview these Key Concepts and keep them in mind as they read the text.

④ **ELL Focus on ELL: Access Content**

BEGINNING SPEAKERS Show students how cells combine and divide during asexual and sexual reproduction by drawing these simple diagrams on the board:

Asexual Reproduction | **Sexual Reproduction**

Parent Cells

Offspring

Color code the drawings of the parent cells and the label "Parent Cells," as well as the offspring cells and their label. Point to the diagrams as you explain why asexual reproduction results in genetically identical offspring while sexual reproduction produces offspring with a combination of genetic information from both parents.

Quick Facts

CELL SIZE

While surface area to volume ratios limit the sizes of cells, not all cells are the same size. In fact, there are a surprising variety of cell sizes that exist in nature. For example, some tiny *Mycoplasma* bacteria measure a scant 0.3 micrometers in diameter. To put that in perspective, it can take hundreds of these bacteria, set end to end, to equal the width of a single human hair, about 50–200 micrometers. On the other extreme, giraffes have nerve cells that stretch for meters along the length of their necks.

Answers

FIGURE 10–3 The offspring share the same genetic material as their parent.

IN YOUR NOTEBOOK Venn diagrams should show the following characteristics: For both sexual and asexual reproduction: produces new organisms; For asexual reproduction only: quick, produces genetically identical offspring, one parent; For sexual reproduction only: offspring produced by the fusion of two cells, two parents

Cell Growth and Division **277**

LESSON 10.1

② **Reading Support Strategies** *(Principles 3 and 4)*

- Watch out for text-dense Student Edition pages that require English language learners to rely heavily on reading comprehension skills.

- Use reading-support and peer-learning strategies, such as Cloze Prompts and Think-Pair-Share activities, to help ELLs better understand these sections. For detailed descriptions of different strategies, see the Teaching Strategies for English Language Learners section in this handbook.

On this page . . .

- Use the Stop and Answer reading support strategy to help your ELLs understand the most important points in this section. For example, after reading the first paragraph, have them stop and answer the question, "Why is reproduction important to living things?" After reading the section headed **Asexual Reproduction,** have them stop and answer the question, "What is asexual reproduction?"

③ **Differentiated Instruction Notes** *(Principle 3)*

- The Differentiated Instruction suggestions in the Teacher's Edition wrap-around offer various ways to modify your instruction for different learner groups. Many of these suggestions may be helpful for ELLs.

- Pay special attention to English Language Learner (ELL) and Less Proficient Reader (LPR) notes.

On this page . . .

- You can use the less proficient reader note on this page to support your English language learners.

- After listing the simplified Key Concepts on the board, read them aloud. Briefly discuss each.

④ **Focus on ELL** *(Principle 3)*

- Focus on ELL boxes provide targeted activities and strategies to help English language learners better understand lesson concepts.

On this page . . .

- Use the teaching suggestion in the Focus on ELL box to provide students with a visual scaffold for the concepts of sexual and asexual reproduction.

- Suggest ELLs copy the labeled diagrams into their notebooks to help them remember the concepts.

Teaching With The Principles

---

① Mystery Clue *(Principle 3)*

- Introduce the Chapter Mystery at the start of each chapter. Then, look for Mystery Clues inside the lessons to help connect the mystery to lesson concepts.

- Chapter Mysteries provide ELLs with an alternate, interesting way to engage in chapter content.

On this page . . .

- Read the Mystery Clue aloud and, if necessary, restate it in simpler terms for beginning speakers.

- Suggest that pairs of ELLs talk about and write an answer to the Mystery Clue. This will give them extra practice listening, speaking, and writing academic language.

Teach continued

 Discuss with students what they think starts to happen to the lost limb of the salamander after a few days. Suggest students look back at the hydra and kalanchoe in **Figure 10–3** for a hint. Students can go online at Biology.com to gather their evidence.

② Assess and Remediate

EVALUATE UNDERSTANDING

Ask students to write a paragraph that explains why a cell in the human body never grows as large as a fist. Then, have them complete the 10.1 Assessment.

REMEDIATION SUGGESTION

L1 Struggling Students If your students have trouble with **Question 1a**, have them go back to the Key Concept on the first page of the lesson. Have them rewrite each part of the Key Concept in "if-then" form.

BIOLOGY.com Students can check their understanding of lesson concepts with the **Self-Test** assessment. They can then take an online version of the **Lesson Assessment**.

---

① MYSTERY CLUE

As its wound heals, the salamander's body cells are dividing to repair the damage. In what way is this type of cell division similar to asexual reproduction?

Comparing Asexual and Sexual Reproduction You can see that each type of reproduction has its advantages and disadvantages when you look at each one as a strategy for survival. Species survive by reproducing. The better suited a species is to its environment, the greater its chance of survival.

For single-celled organisms, asexual reproduction is a survival strategy. When conditions are right, the faster they reproduce, the better their chance of survival over other organisms using the same resources. Having offspring that are genetically identical is also an advantage as long as conditions remain favorable. However, a lack of genetic diversity becomes a disadvantage when conditions change in ways that do not fit the characteristics of an organism.

Sexual reproduction is a different type of survival strategy. The process of finding a mate and the growth and development of offspring require more time. However, this can be an advantage for species that live in environments where seasonal changes affect weather conditions and food availability. Sexual reproduction also provides genetic diversity. If an environment changes, some offspring may have the right combination of characteristics needed to survive.

Some organisms reproduce both sexually and asexually. Yeasts, for example, are single-celled eukaryotes that use both strategies. They reproduce asexually most of the time. However, under certain conditions, they enter a sexual phase. The different advantages of each type of reproduction may help to explain why the living world includes organisms that reproduce sexually, those that reproduce asexually, and many organisms that do both.

10.1 Assessment

Review Key Concepts

1. a. Review Identify two reasons why a cell's growth is limited.
b. Explain As a cell's size increases, what happens to the ratio of its surface area to its volume?
c. Applying Concepts Why is a cell's surface area-to-volume ratio important?
2. a. Review What is asexual reproduction? What is sexual reproduction?
b. Explain What types of organisms reproduce sexually?
c. Summarize What are the advantages and disadvantages of both asexual and sexual reproduction?

VISUAL THINKING   MATH

3. The formula for finding the surface area of a sphere, such as a baseball or a basketball, is $A = 4\pi r^2$, where r is the radius. The formula for finding the volume of a sphere is $V = 4/3\pi r^3$.
a. Calculate Calculate the surface area and the volume of the baseball and the basketball. Then, write the ratio of surface area to volume for each sphere.
b. Infer If the baseball and basketball were cells, which would possess a larger ratio of area of cell membrane to cell volume?

$r = 12.2$ cm

$r = 3.6$ cm

BIOLOGY.com Search (Lesson 10.1) GO • Self-Test • Lesson Assessment

278 Chapter 10 • Lesson 1

Assessment Answers

1a. The larger a cell becomes, the more demands it places on its DNA and the more trouble it has moving enough nutrients and wastes across the cell membrane.

1b. As a cell grows, its surface area-to-volume ratio decreases.

1c. As a cell's volume grows, its membrane needs more and more surface area to bring nutrients, oxygen, and water into the cell and move waste out. The cell's surface area-to-volume ratio shows how much area is available to move materials in and out of the cell compared to the cell's volume.

2a. Asexual reproduction is the production of offspring from only one parent. Sexual reproduction is the production of offspring from two parents.

2b. Most animals and plants reproduce sexually, as do some single-celled organisms.

2c. Asexual reproduction occurs rapidly, enabling a population to increase rapidly; however, the offspring are genetically identical and may not survive a change in the environment. Sexual reproduction takes longer, so a population does not grow fast; however, the offspring have a mix of genetic material from two parents that might help the population survive if the environment changes.

VISUAL THINKING

3a. baseball, 0.85:1; basketball, 0.25:1

3b. the baseball

---

② Assessment Options *(Principle 5)*

- To assess your English language learners, look through the various options offered by *Miller & Levine Biology* and find the most appropriate assessment tool.

- Use the Evaluate Understanding suggestion in the Teacher's Edition wrap-around as a quick, informal lesson assessment tool.

- For a performance-based alternative assessment, check the Evidence of Understanding activity found in the Teach for Understanding box on the first page of each lesson.

- For a visually based assessment tool, check the *Assessment Resources Book* to see if there is a Visual Quiz associated with the lesson you are teaching.

- To help students assess their own understanding, suggest they take the Self-Test on **Biology.com**.

- For ELLs who find it easier to type their answers than write them, suggest they take the Lesson Assessment online at **Biology.com**.

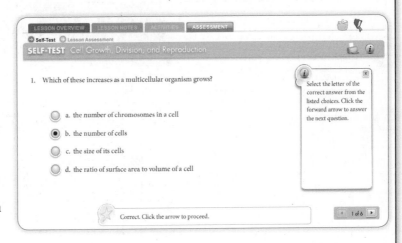

On this page . . .

- Have ELLs complete the 10.1 Self-Test to evaluate their own understanding of lesson concepts. If they struggle with any questions, suggest they review the material with a partner.

- Assign the 10.1 Assessment. Simplify difficult questions for beginning and intermediate speakers. For example, for question 3, write the formulas below on the board and have ELLs use them to answer questions 3a and 3b.

  radius = r

  Surface area of sphere: $A = 4\pi r^2$

  Volume of sphere: $V = \frac{4}{3}\pi r^3$

Teaching ELLs With *Miller & Levine Biology: Foundation Edition*

Many of the features in *Miller & Levine Biology: Foundation Edition* align closely with the five principles. For example, the Teacher's Edition has been specifically designed to support both reading instruction and content acquisition. Additionally, the Foundation Student Edition covers all the same concepts as the mainstream book, but it is written at a lower, more-accessible reading level.

You can use all of the targeted language support features in the Foundation Edition to enhance the learning experience of your ELLs. Follow the model lesson to identify both the built-in ELL scaffolds and places in the text where your English language learners might need extra support.

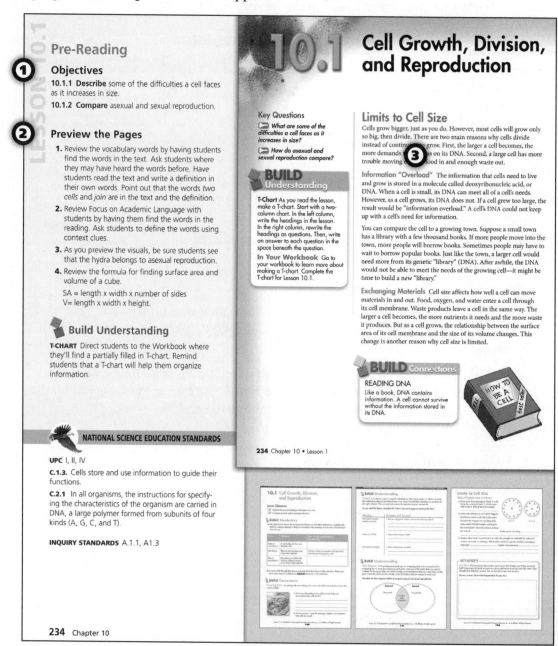

① Content Objectives *(Principle 1)*

- Use the content objectives to preview lesson concepts.
- Lesson objectives are also listed in *Study Workbook B.*

On this page . . .

- Ask a student to write objective 10.1.1 on the board, read it aloud, and circle *Describe.* To confirm that students understand this academic vocabulary term, ask someone to describe a classroom object.
- Ask another student to write objective 10.1.2 on the board, read it aloud, and circle *Compare.* Ask someone to compare two classroom objects.

② Preview the Pages *(Principle 2)*

- Look for Preview the Pages margin features at the beginning of each lesson in the Teacher's Edition wrap-around. Use the list to help frontload content for ELLs.

On this page . . .

- Have students preview the pages by following the list of suggested items, focusing on lesson vocabulary and visuals.
- Suggest students find the vocabulary terms in the text. Read each term aloud and have students repeat after you. Then, have them define each term in their own words. Encourage beginning speakers to draw a representation of the terms.
- Have pairs of students work together to preview lesson visuals. After looking at each visual, suggest they make a prediction about what they might learn.

③ Difficult Terms *(Principles 1 and 4)*

- Scan the Student Edition for terms that ELLs may not be familiar with but will need to know to understand lesson content. Provide language support for these terms.

On this page . . .

- Write the terms *overload, membrane, waste product,* and *nutrients* on the board. Have students provide an example sentence and visual for each term.
- If desired, provide additional background for the terms. For example, introduce the term *overload* by creating a demonstration, such as a glass overflowing with water. As the amount of water grows, the demand on the glass becomes too great.

Teaching With The Principles

---

① ## Cultural Context *(Principle 2)*

- Be aware of historic, cultural, or societal factors with which non-native English language learners may be unfamiliar. Provide them with the background knowledge they need to understand the content.

On this page . . .

- The visual assumes students know the typical structure of American cities. If needed, explain that most U.S. cities have a library, fire station, and so on.

- Encourage non-native ELLs to explain or draw the typical community structure in their native countries.

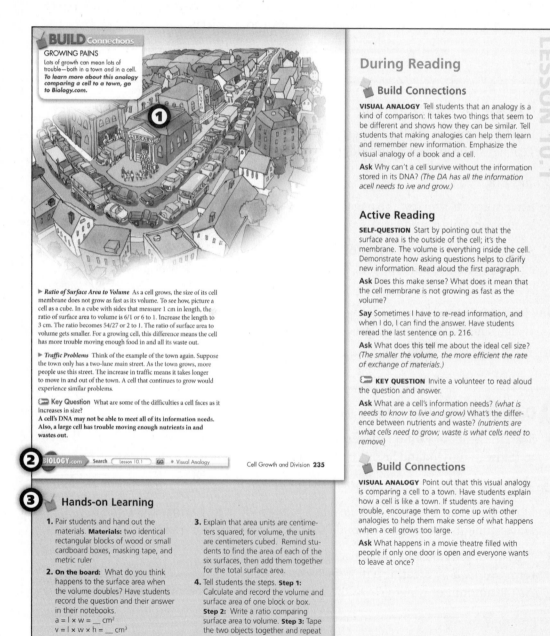

BUILD Connections

GROWING PAINS

Lots of growth can mean lots of trouble—both in a town and in a cell. *To learn more about this analogy comparing a cell to a town, go to Biology.com.*

①

▶ ***Ratio of Surface Area to Volume*** As a cell grows, the size of its cell membrane does not grow as fast as its volume. To see how, picture a cell as a cube. In a cube with sides that measure 1 cm in length, the ratio of surface area to volume is 6/1 or 6 to 1. Increase the length to 3 cm. The ratio becomes 54/27 or 2 to 1. The ratio of surface area to volume gets smaller. For a growing cell, this difference means the cell has more trouble moving enough food in and all its waste out.

▶ ***Traffic Problems*** Think of the example of the town again. Suppose the town only has a two-lane main street. As the town grows, more people use this street. The increase in traffic means it takes longer to move in and out of the town. A cell that continues to grow would experience similar problems.

Key Question What are some of the difficulties a cell faces as it increases in size?
A cell's DNA may not be able to meet all of its information needs. Also, a large cell has trouble moving enough nutrients in and wastes out.

② **BIOLOGY.com** ▶ Search [Lesson 10.1] **GO** ▸ Visual Analogy   Cell Growth and Division **235**

③ ## Hands-on Learning

1. Pair students and hand out the materials. **Materials:** two identical rectangular blocks of wood or small cardboard boxes, masking tape, and metric ruler.

2. **On the board:** What do you think happens to the surface area when the volume doubles? Have students record the question and their answer in their notebooks.
$a = l \times w = \_\_ cm^2$
$v = l \times w \times h = \_\_ cm^3$

3. Explain that area units are centimeters squared; for volume, the units are centimeters cubed. Remind students to find the area of each of the six surfaces, then add them together for the total surface area.

4. Tell students the steps. **Step 1:** Calculate and record the volume and surface area of one block or box. **Step 2:** Write a ratio comparing surface area to volume. **Step 3:** Tape the two objects together and repeat Steps 1 and 2. **Step 4:** Evaluate your findings in your notebook.

During Reading

Build Connections

VISUAL ANALOGY Tell students that an analogy is a kind of comparison: It takes two things that seem to be different and shows how they can be similar. Tell students that making analogies can help them learn and remember new information. Emphasize the visual analogy of a book and a cell.

Ask Why can't a cell survive without the information stored in its DNA? *(The DA has all the information acell needs to ive and grow.)*

Active Reading

SELF-QUESTION Start by pointing out that the surface area is the outside of the cell; it's the membrane. The volume is everything inside the cell. Demonstrate how asking questions helps to clarify new information. Read aloud the first paragraph.

Ask Does this make sense? What does it mean that the cell membrane is not growing as fast as the volume?

Say Sometimes I have to re-read information, and when I do, I can find the answer. Have students reread the last sentence on p. 216.

Ask What does this tell me about the ideal cell size? *(The smaller the volume, the more efficient the rate of exchange of materials.)*

KEY QUESTION Invite a volunteer to read aloud the question and answer.

Ask What are a cell's information needs? *(what is needs to know to live and grow)* What's the difference between nutrients and waste? *(nutrients are what cells need to grow; waste is what cells need to remove)*

Build Connections

VISUAL ANALOGY Point out that this visual analogy is comparing a cell to a town. Have students explain how a cell is like a town. If students are having trouble, encourage them to come up with other analogies to help make sense of what happens when a cell grows too large.

Ask What happens in a movie theatre filled with people if only one door is open and everyone wants to leave at once?

Cell Growth and Division **235**

② Digital Support *(Principle 3)*

- Look for **Biology.com** activities that provide English language learners with comprehensible input and alternate ways to access content.

On this page . . .

- Use the Student Edition to present the Build Connections visual analogy to your class. Make sure ELLs understand the basic premise of the analogy: the library is analogous to a cell nucleus, while traffic is analogous to the exchange of materials in a cell.

- Suggest ELLs log on to **Biology.com** and complete the Visual Analogy: Growing Pains activity. Consider pairing beginning speakers with more-proficient speakers to work through the online activity and questions together.

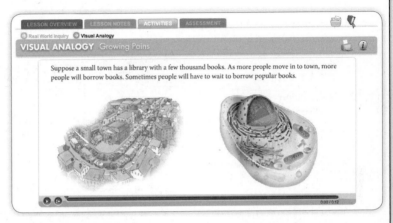

- If students are struggling to complete the activity, suggest they review cell structures, focusing on the cell membrane and nucleus.

③ Hands-on Learning *(Principle 3)*

- Look for Hands-on Learning activities in the Teacher's Edition wrap-around. Use them to provide ELLs with engaging, hands-on explorations of lesson concepts.

On this page . . .

- Have students complete the hands-on learning activity.

- Before beginning the activity, determine if students need additional background knowledge on the math terms *ratio*, *surface area*, and *volume*.

- Use real-life objects and a demonstration to clarify the meanings of the terms as well the formulas for determining them.

Teaching With The Principles

① Enable Language Production
(Principle 4)

- Look for Active Reading notes in the Teacher's Edition wrap-around to teach and practice reading, listening, and speaking skills.

On this page . . .

- Apply the Active Reading strategy described on the page below.

- Have ELLs use other reading strategies, such as Stop and Answer. For example, after reading the first two paragraphs, have ELLs stop and answer, "How can cell division be a form of reproduction?"

LESSON 10.1

① During Reading continued

Active Reading

VISUALIZE/DIAGRAM Point out how helpful it is to sketch ideas so that they make sense. Draw and label the following diagram on the board. Have students copy it into their notebooks.

Asexual Reproduction   Sexual Reproduction

Parent Cells

Offspring

Point to the diagrams as you explain why asexual reproduction results in genetically identical offspring while sexual reproduction produces offspring with a combination of genetic information from both parents.

Build Vocabulary

PREFIXES Have students pronounce each vocabulary word and read the definition. Then have them find the word and the definition in the text.

Point out the prefix a– means *without* as in asexual reproduction.

Ask What is asexual reproduction doing "without"? *(without a second cell)*

④ Speed Bump

Ask Can a cell keep growing forever? *(no)*

Ask Why do cells divide? What are the two main reasons? *(1. When a cell grows larger, its DNA does not, so the cell ends up making more demands on its DNA. 2. The larger the cell, the harder it is for the cell to exchange food and waste.)*

Ask In this lesson, what do the ratios compare? *(The ratios compare the cell's surface area to its volume.)*

Ask Is it better for a cell to be smaller in size or larger? Why? *(Smaller size is better; a smaller cell can more efficiently exchange materials across cell membrane.)*

---

② BUILD Vocabulary

cell division
a process by which a cell divides into two new daughter cells

asexual reproduction
a process by which a single parent reproduces by itself

sexual reproduction
a process by which two cells from different parents fuse, or join together, to produce the first cell of a new organism

🔖 PREFIXES
The prefix *a–* in *asexual* means "without." Asexual reproduction is reproduction without the fusion of cells.

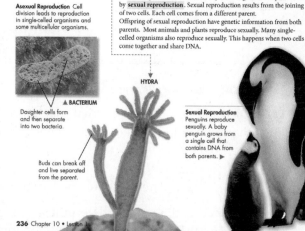

Asexual Reproduction Cell division leads to reproduction in single-celled organisms and some multicellular organisms.

▲ **BACTERIUM**

Daughter cells form and then separate into two bacteria.

HYDRA

Buds can break off and live separated from the parent.

Sexual Reproduction Penguins reproduce sexually. A baby penguin grows from a single cell that contains DNA from both parents. ▶

236 Chapter 10 • Lesson 1

Cell Division and Reproduction

Before it becomes too large, a growing cell divides. The two new cells are referred to as "daughter" cells. The process by which a cell divides into two cells is called **cell division**.

During the process of cell division, a cell makes a copy of its DNA. Each daughter cell gets its own copy. This solves the problem of information overload. Cell division also decreases a cell's volume. This allows for a better exchange of materials in and out of the cell. Cell division can also result in reproduction. Reproduction is the process by which organisms produce offspring—new organisms.

Asexual Reproduction For an organism made up of just one cell, cell division may be the only form of reproduction it needs. All the organism has to do is to copy its DNA and then divide. Reproduction by a single parent is called **asexual reproduction**. Offspring of asexual reproduction have the same genetic information as their parent.

Many multicellular organisms reproduce asexually. Hydras are small animals that live in ponds. They reproduce asexually by budding. As cells divide, the bud grows. The bud eventually separates from the parent. A hydra budding is shown below.

Sexual Reproduction Another way for an organism to reproduce is by **sexual reproduction**. Sexual reproduction results from the joining of two cells. Each cell comes from a different parent. Offspring of sexual reproduction have genetic information from both parents. Most animals and plants reproduce sexually. Many single-celled organisms also reproduce sexually. This happens when two cells come together and share DNA.

---

③ Focus on Academic Language

- multicellular   • advantage   • well suited for   • ideal conditions   • adjust

Review with students the meaning of *multicellular* (having many cells). Explain that the prefix *multi-* means *many*.

Ask Can you guess what these words mean? *multiplex* (theater with many screens); *multitask* (do many tasks at the same time); *multitalented* (having many talents); *multiple* (many parts).

Write *advantage, well suited for, ideal conditions,* and *adjust* on the board. Pair students and have them find the words in their reading of the paragraph "Advantages." Have them predict the meaning using context clues and explain their reasoning in their notebooks.

236 Chapter 10

2 Content Vocabulary *(Principle 1)*

- Look for Build Vocabulary features in the Student Edition. These boxes provide a definition of each content vocabulary term on the page where it first appears.

On this page . . .

- Pronounce each term in the Build Vocabulary box and have students repeat them. Suggest students read through the terms, definitions, and how they are used in context within the paragraphs. Ask students to give definitions in their own words and draw a visual for each term.

- Point out the prefixes note in the Build Vocabulary feature. Discuss what a prefix is and how prefixes can affect the meaning of English words.

- Have students either complete or review the Build Vocabulary chart in *Study Workbook B*.

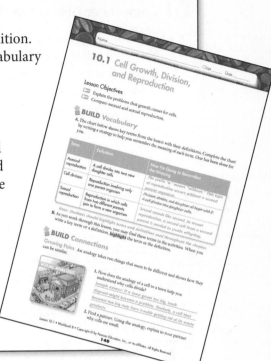

3 Academic Vocabulary *(Principle 1)*

- To improve students' academic vocabulary, use the Focus on Academic Language boxes in the Teacher's Edition wrap-around.

On this page . . .

- Introduce the terms listed in the Focus on Academic Language box. Follow the teaching suggestions to ensure your English language learners understand what each term means.

4 Formative Assessment *(Principle 5)*

- Use the Speed Bumps in the Teacher's Edition wrap-around to informally check your English language learners' comprehension of lesson concepts.

- Use the results to diagnose strengths and challenges and to inform instruction.

On this page . . .

- Write the Speed Bump questions on the board and read them aloud for your ELLs.

- Have pairs of ELLs discuss the questions and write down their responses. Then, have them take turns providing answers orally.

Teaching With The Principles

① **Comprehensible Input** *(Principle 3)*

- Look for opportunities to make lesson concepts more accessible to English language learners. For example, have students use images, charts, tables, and graphic organizers.

On this page . . .

- Point out the Build Understanding note on this page.

- Draw a Venn diagram on the board and complete it using two familiar topics, such as a cat and a dog. Then, have students complete the Build Understanding Venn diagram in *Study Workbook B.*

Advantages Each method of reproduction has advantages. The main advantages of asexual reproduction are that it is quick and it produces genetically identical offspring. An organism that is well suited for its environment can reproduce very quickly. The result is a large number of equally well-suited offspring. This is one reason why bacteria are able to grow so quickly when they find themselves in ideal conditions.

The main advantage of sexual reproduction is that offspring are genetically different from their parents. Sexual reproduction lets species "try out" new combinations of genetic information from one generation to the next. If the environment changes rapidly, some members of a species may be able to adjust to those changes.

Disadvantages Each method of reproduction also has disadvantages. Sexual reproduction is generally slower than asexual reproduction since it takes two parents instead of one to produce offspring. In asexual reproduction, the lack of genetic diversity can be a disadvantage. Asexually reproducing organisms may not have characteristics needed if their environment changes rapidly.

Key Question How do asexual and sexual reproduction compare?
Asexual reproduction involves one parent—offspring have the same genetic material as the parent. Sexual reproduction involves two parents—offspring inherit genetic material from both parents.

① BUILD Understanding

Venn Diagram Use a Venn diagram to compare and contrast asexual and sexual reproduction.

In Your Workbook Go to your workbook to learn more about making a Venn diagram. Complete the Venn diagram started for you.

---

② ✔CHECK Understanding

Apply Vocabulary
Use the highlighted words from the lesson to complete each sentence correctly.

1. For a growing cell, _____ solves the problems of overloading DNA and not being able to get enough materials in or out.
2. Offspring produced by _____ have a mix of DNA from two parents.
3. Cell division in a single-celled organism is a form of _____.

Critical Thinking

3. Compare and Contrast How does DNA in offspring produced by asexual reproduction compare to DNA.

5. Apply Concepts Describe advantages and disadvantages of asexual reproduction. Describe advantages and disadvantages of sexual reproduction.
6. Write to Learn Answer the first clue of the mystery. Write a paragraph that includes the terms *DNA, cell division.*

③ MYSTERY CLUE

What is happening to the cells in the salamander's leg? Is this cell division or asexual reproduction?

Cell Growth and Division **237**

Active Reading

MAKING INFERENCES Read aloud the first two paragraphs.

Ask Have you ever heard of strep throat? It's a bad sore throat caused by the bacteria Streptococcus. Strep throat is highly contagious — you can catch it easily. Strep throat can spread quickly through a school. Why? *(Bacteria are organisms that reproduce asexually; under the right conditions, they multiply quickly.)*

KEY QUESTION Read aloud the Key Question. Ask What's the key word that can help you begin your answer? *(compare)* If you saw this question on a test, what should you do first? *(Answers will vary but should include a graphic organizer.)* Have students refer to their Venn diagrams and answer the question in complete sentences in their notebooks.

Build Understanding

Have students finish the Venn diagram in their notebooks.

Post Reading

ASSESSMENT TIPS Review the highlighted vocabulary words with students before they begin the assessment.

For question 5, pair students. Ask them to create a graphic organizer that will help them answer the question. Then using the graphic organizer, have them answer the question in complete sentences.

MYSTERY CLUE Discuss with students what they think happens to the missing limb of the salamander after a few days. *(As its wound heals, the salamander's body cells are dividing to repair the damage.)*

Wrap Up Activity

COMPOSE A TEST Preparing an actual test is a valuable strategy in helping students identify the most relevant information in the lesson. Divide students into small groups. Each group is responsible for writing one test with five multiple-choice items including four options for each item; or five fill-in-the-blanks; or five matching; and one constructed response. Each group passes its test until each group has another groups' test to answer. Eventually, each test is given back to the group who originated the test to be corrected.

Check Understanding

1. cell division
2. sexual reproduction
3. asexual reproduction
4. Offspring produced by asexual reproduction have the same DNA as their parent and are genetically the same. Offspring produced by sexual reproduction have the DNA of both parents; they are genetically different from their parents.

5. Advantages of sexual reproduction: offspring are genetically different, which allows species to survive in case of a changing environment. Disadvantages: need two parents and is slower. Advantages of asexual reproduction: it's quick; needs only one parent. Disadvantages: lack of genetic diversity.
6. Answers will vary.

Cell Growth and Division **237**

② **Assessment Options** *(Principle 5)*

- *Miller & Levine Biology: Foundation Edition* offers various assessment options. Choose the most appropriate tool for your ELLs.

- Use the Check Understanding feature as an assessment tool to gauge students' understanding of lesson concepts.

- For a performance-based alternative assessment, check the Wrap Up Activity found on the last page of each lesson in the Teacher's Edition wrap-around.

- For a visually based assessment tool, check the *Assessment Resources Book* to see if there is a visual quiz that will test your students on lesson concepts.

On this page . . .

- Assign the 10.1 Check Understanding. Suggest students work in small groups to complete the Critical Thinking section. They should discuss the answers and compose written responses together.

③ **Mystery Clue** *(Principle 3)*

- Chapter Mysteries provide ELLs with an alternate, interesting way to engage in chapter content.

- Introduce the Chapter Mystery before you start teaching each chapter. Use the Mystery Clues to help connect the mystery to lesson concepts.

On this page . . .

- Read the Mystery Clue aloud and, if necessary, restate it in simpler terms for beginning speakers.

- Discuss the Mystery Clue as a class to give ELLs extra practice listening to and speaking academic language.

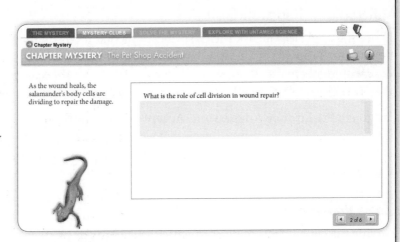

Teaching Strategies for English Language Learners

The following list of teaching strategies can help you differentiate the content of *Miller & Levine Biology* for your English language learners. While the Teacher's Edition has identified places where these strategies may be particularly useful, you will likely find many other opportunities to apply them in your class.

There are four basic types of strategies:

> **Reading Support Strategies** provide support for students as they interact with the text and lesson concepts.

> **Vocabulary Strategies** help students who are struggling to learn and comprehend lesson vocabulary terms.

> **Peer Learning Strategies** promote cooperative learning. Beginning and intermediate speakers are able to hear and see concepts presented in different ways, while more advanced speakers benefit by teaching lesson concepts.

> **Organizing Information Strategies** provide students with a scaffolded way to organize lesson information. Often the strategies involve using a graphic organizer.

> **Comprehension Check Strategies** allow teachers to monitor student understanding in an ongoing manner. At a glance teachers can see how many students understand and how many do not.

Reading Support Strategies

Anticipation/Reaction Guide

Before starting a lesson, ask the class questions that focus on lesson topics. While the questions can address topics that have not yet been covered, make sure they require students to access some prior knowledge. After the lesson, have students re-answer the questions and compare how their answers have changed.

Language Proficiency Adaptation Accept relevant terms or short phrases from beginning speakers. Require intermediate and advanced speakers to write full-sentence responses. Encourage all ELLs to read their answers aloud so that they can practice speaking in English.

Cloze Prompts

Provide the class with sentences in which key words or phrases have been replaced with blanks. As students work through the lesson, they should fill in the blanks with the correct terms or phrases.

Language Proficiency Adaptation Provide beginning speakers with word banks to help them complete the cloze prompts. Challenge advanced speakers to create their own cloze prompt sentences and then trade with a partner to help them review lesson concepts.

Directed Reading-Thinking Activity (DR-TA)

This strategy teaches students to make predictions, read to acquire lesson concepts, and then follow up with a review. Have students follow these steps:

- Skim the headings, images, and vocabulary in the text.
- Make a prediction of what the reading is about.
- Read the text.
- At teacher-defined stopping points, compare predictions with concepts and information learned in the lesson.
- Revise predictions.

Language Proficiency Adaptation For beginning speakers, stop more frequently to compare predictions with what students have learned. Give them additional time to respond to what they have read.

KWL

KWL charts help students activate prior knowledge, gather information, and check for understanding.

To fill in a KWL chart:

- Before the lesson, have students fill in the K and W columns.
- K column: students write what they **Know** about the topic.
- W column: students write what they **Want** to know about the topic.
- After the lesson, have students fill in the L column.
- L column: students write what they **Learned** about the topic.

KWL charts can be modified to include a **Background** section at the beginning—these are BKWL charts. Use a BKWL chart when you provide students with background information about the lesson. Students can take notes in this column. You may also wish to add an R column after the L column for students to list topics for future **Research.**

Language Proficiency Adaptation Accept drawings and relevant terms or phrases from beginning speakers. For intermediate speakers, encourage them to write in full sentences. Require advanced speakers to write in full sentences. Check their questions for correct sentence structure.

Background	I Know	I Want to know	I Learned

*Use the graphic organizer (GO11 KWL and GO12 BKWL) in the **Transparencies** book to present this strategy.*

Lesson Preview

Have students preview the lesson by skimming topic headings, diagrams, pictures, vocabulary, and key concepts. Then, have students write down or discuss what they think the lesson will be about.

Language Proficiency Adaptation Give English language learners additional time to discuss their predictions with one another. If desired, pair beginning and intermediate speakers with advanced or native English speakers.

Question-Answer Relationships (QAR)

Students learn to recognize four different types of questions so that they can better answer them. After working through a lesson, have students answer and/or write questions of each type.

- *Right There:* answers are found directly in the text.
- *Think and Search:* answers come from finding information in different parts of the text and fitting these ideas together.
- *Author and You:* answers are inferred—they are a mix of students' own knowledge and the author's writing.
- *On My Own:* answers are composed of students' own knowledge.

Language Proficiency Adaptation Have beginning and intermediate speakers work together to answer questions of each type. Suggest they break the activity into steps. First, have them read the question and confirm what it is asking. Then, have them label the question with its type. Finally, suggest they write the answer. For advanced speakers, have them both answer and write questions of each type.

Quick Write

Give students a short period of time (one, five, or ten minutes) to write everything they know about a topic. Encourage them to write continuously about the topic for the entire time, even if they have to repeat a fact several times.

Language Proficiency Adaptation Accept drawings and/or bulleted lists from beginning speakers.

Stop and Answer

Write a list of sequential questions on the board. Next to the question, indicate when each question should be answered. As students read the lesson or discuss a concept, stop them at the specified points and have them answer the questions.

Language Proficiency Adaptation Encourage all English language learners to discuss the questions with one another. These discussions will give them extra opportunities to practice their speaking and listening skills.

Vocabulary Strategies

Frayer Model

The Frayer model helps students understand a vocabulary term by having them examine its definition, characteristics, examples, and non-examples.

To fill in a Frayer model:

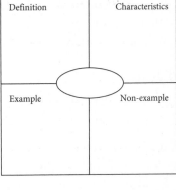

- Write the vocabulary term in the center oval.

- Write the definition, brainstorm characteristics, and provide examples of the term in the appropriate boxes.

- In the non-example box, list things that are not examples of the term, but are similar in some way. For example, if the term is "the carbon cycle," students may list another biogeochemical cycle.

Language Proficiency Adaptation For English language learners who are proficient in writing in their native language, have them use the bottom right box (non-examples) to define the term in their native language. You may also choose to permit drawings in the "characteristics" box.

Use the graphic organizers (GO9 Frayer Model and GO10 ELL Frayer Model) in the **Transparencies** *book to present this strategy.*

Vocabulary Word Map

This graphic organizer helps students learn vocabulary by associating the terms with related words and images.

To fill in a vocabulary word map:

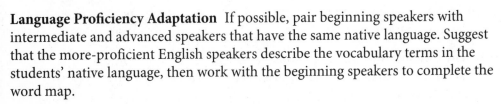

- Write the vocabulary term in the top box.

- Fill in the bottom boxes with terms, phrases, or images that are associated with the vocabulary term.

Language Proficiency Adaptation If possible, pair beginning speakers with intermediate and advanced speakers that have the same native language. Suggest that the more-proficient English speakers describe the vocabulary terms in the students' native language, then work with the beginning speakers to complete the word map.

Use the graphic organizer (GO17) in the **Transparencies** *book to present this strategy.*

Word Wall

Designate a wall in your classroom to be used as a word wall. Add key vocabulary and difficult words, along with their definitions, for the entire class to reference. Encourage students to contribute to the word wall.

Language Proficiency Adaptation Support beginning and intermediate speakers by suggesting they write down words for you to define and post. Encourage students to add definitions in their native languages.

Peer Learning Strategies

Core Concept Discussion

Divide the class into small groups. Have each student identify a core concept—a main idea or lesson topic—to discuss within his or her group. After small-group discussions, have the class talk about at least one core concept from each group.

Language Proficiency Adaptation Make sure English language learners at all proficiency levels take an active role in both the group and class discussions. Encourage advanced speakers to take a leadership role.

Debate

Divide the class into two groups. Assign each group a position to argue regarding a discussion topic. If desired, give groups time to research and plan their arguments.

Language Proficiency Adaptation Make sure groups contain a mix of students at different language proficiency levels. Encourage all English language learners to take an active role in the debate.

Gallery Walk

In a gallery walk, small groups of students work together to respond to posted prompts and review the responses of other groups.

- Post chart-paper stations around the classroom, each displaying a concept or question for groups to respond to.

- Divide the class into groups and assign each group a different color to write with. The number of groups should equal the number of stations.

- Have each group walk to a station and respond to the posted question or prompt.

- Groups should then circulate through the stations, or "gallery." At each station, have them evaluate the previous groups' answers, making any necessary corrections or comments, and adding any relevant information.

- When groups return to their original stations, have them work together to summarize the information on their charts.

Language Proficiency Adaptation Arrange students so that each group contains a mix of students at different language proficiency levels. Encourage beginning speakers to contribute both orally and, if appropriate, in writing.

Jigsaw Review

In a jigsaw review, each student is responsible for teaching a concept to a small group of students. Divide the class into learning circles. The number of students in each learning circle should equal the number of concepts you will assign students to review. Assign each student in a learning circle a number. Have students with the same number join to form a study group. For example, all the 2's should work together. Then, assign each study group a different concept or topic to review. Study groups should create a lesson plan to teach the concept. Have students return to their original learning circles and take turns teaching their lessons.

Language Proficiency Adaptation Encourage beginning speakers to create and present visual aids to their learning circles.

Problem and Solution

Present students with a problem. Have small groups discuss the problem and propose a solution. Each group should share their solution with the class. Have the class compare and contrast the different solutions.

Language Proficiency Adaptation Make sure groups contain a mix of students at different language proficiency levels. Encourage all English language learners to take an active role in both group and class discussions.

Reader-Writer-Speaker Response

In this strategy, students discuss a question or topic in groups of three. Each group member plays a different role. The *Reader* reads about the topic, the *Writer* records the discussion, and the *Speaker* shares the group's comments with the class.

Language Proficiency Adaptation Make sure groups contain a mix of students at different language proficiency levels. Suggest advanced speakers assume the role that will challenge them most. For example, if a student is a more proficient English writer than speaker, encourage him or her to be the group *Speaker*.

Think-Pair-Share

Give students a question or topic to think about individually. Next, have pairs of students discuss the topic. Pairs should then share their comments with the class or with another pair.

Language Proficiency Adaptation If possible, pair beginning and intermediate speakers with more advanced or native English speakers.

Topic Circles

Arrange the class in small-group circles. Introduce a topic or idea. Then, have one member of each circle give a fact or detail about the topic being discussed. The student to their right should then provide a different fact or detail. The cycle should continue until there is no more new information to share.

Language Proficiency Adaptation Allow beginning and intermediate speakers extra time to share their facts and details. You may also wish to permit beginning speakers to refer to their books or notes during the discussion.

Organizing Information Strategies

Timeline

Have students create a timeline to display events that have occurred in a sequential order. Suggest they show the passage of time as a straight line with important events and discoveries marked along the way.

Language Proficiency Adaptation For the timeline descriptions, accept relevant terms or short phrases from beginning speakers.

Cause and Effect Diagram

To visually represent cause-and-effect relationships, suggest students make and fill out cause-and-effect diagrams. Reinforce that a single cause can have multiple effects, just as several causes can contribute to a single effect.

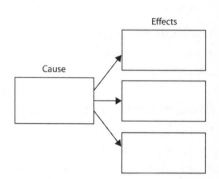

Language Proficiency Adaptation Provide support for beginning speakers by supplying word/phrase banks.

*Use the graphic organizer (GO1) in the **Transparencies** book to present this strategy.*

Cluster Diagram

Have students show how concepts are related by making a cluster diagram.

To create a cluster diagram:

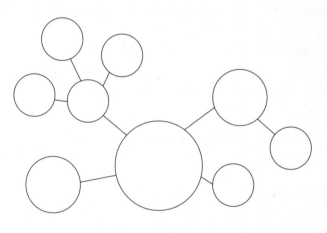

- Write the main idea or topic on a sheet of paper. Circle it.

- Draw lines branching off the main idea, connected to circles that contain concepts or characteristics related to the main topic.

- Continue adding facts and details in a branching pattern, connecting related ideas and facts.

Language Proficiency Adaptation If possible, pair beginning and advanced speakers with the same native language. Allow them to brainstorm in their native language and then work together on their diagrams.

*Use the graphic organizer (GO2) in the **Transparencies** book to present this strategy.*

Compare/Contrast Table

A compare/contrast table helps students organize the similarities and differences between two or more concepts, objects, or processes.

To create a compare/contrast table:

- Draw a table.
- Label the columns with the items being compared.
- Label the rows with the characteristics being examined.
- Fill in the boxes with the characteristics of each item.

Language Proficiency Adaptation Provide beginning speakers with a partially filled-in table and/or a word bank to help them complete their tables.

	Item 1	Item 2	Item 3
Characteristic 1			
Characteristic 2			

*Use the graphic organizer (GO3) in the **Transparencies** book to present this strategy.*

Concept Map

A concept map helps students organize concepts using visual relationships and linking words. Mapping out these connections helps students think about how information fits together.

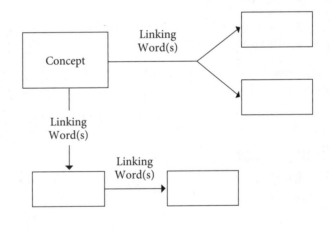

To create a concept map:

- Draw a box and write the main concept inside it.
- Draw arrows to additional boxes. Use linking words along the arrow lines to describe the relationships between connected boxes.
- In the second set of boxes, write details that support the main concept.
- Continue to add boxes and linking words as necessary to further organize details and facts.

Language Proficiency Adaptation If possible, pair beginning and advanced speakers with the same native language. Allow them to brainstorm in their native language and then work together on their concept maps.

*Use the graphic organizer (GO4) in the **Transparencies** book to present this strategy.*

Cornell Notes

Cornell notes is a note-taking strategy for outlining lesson concepts. The Cornell notes strategy helps students identify and list key words. Additionally, it requires students to summarize lesson concepts.

Language Proficiency Adaptation Encourage English language learners to list any terms that they are unfamiliar with in the left-hand column. Suggest they write a definition for each listed term.

*Use the graphic organizer (GO5) in the **Transparencies** book to present this strategy.*

Cycle Diagram

Have students use a cycle diagram to show the steps involved in a repeating process.

To create a cycle diagram:

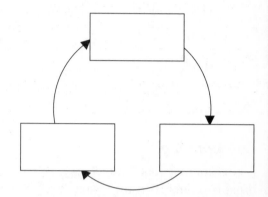

- Draw a box. Fill in the first step of the cycle.

- Draw an arrow to a second box and fill in the next step of the cycle.

- Continue adding boxes in a circular pattern for every step of the cycle. Connect the steps with arrows.

- The last box of the cycle should have an arrow connecting it to the first.

Language Proficiency Adaptation Allow beginning speakers to use drawings and other visual aids in their cycle diagrams.

*Use the graphic organizer (GO6) in the **Transparencies** book to present this strategy.*

Fishbone Map

A fishbone map helps students organize complex topics into main ideas and supporting details.

To create a fishbone map:

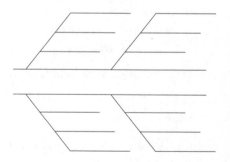

- Draw a "backbone," or set of horizontal lines, and fill them in with a topic.

- Draw diagonal lines that extend off of this backbone. Label each of these diagonals with a main idea related to the topic.

- Draw several lines branching off each diagonal. Write details that support each main idea on these lines.

Language Proficiency Adaptation Allow beginning speakers to work in pairs. Encourage intermediate speakers to work independently at first, and then share their work with another student, revising their fishbone map as necessary.

*Use the graphic organizer (GO7) in the **Transparencies** book to present this strategy.*

Flowchart

Students can use a flowchart to show a sequence of steps or events in a process. Make sure students understand that a flowchart can have one or more paths.

To create a flowchart:

- Write the first step of a process inside a box.
- Use an arrow to connect this first box with a second box that contains the next step in the process.
- Continue connecting boxes until all steps of the process are represented.

Language Proficiency Adaptation Encourage beginning speakers to use drawings and other visual aids in their flowcharts.

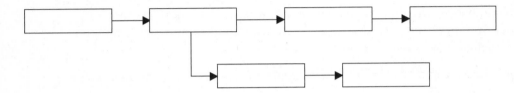

*Use the graphic organizer (GO8) in the **Transparencies** book to present this strategy.*

Main Ideas and Details Chart

Students can use this chart to organize lesson concepts by main ideas and supporting details. Advise them to use clues from the text such as headings and topic sentences to determine main ideas.

To create a main ideas and details chart:

- Draw a line down the center of a sheet of paper to divide it into two columns.
- In the left column, write the main ideas of the topic or reading.
- In the right column, write the supporting details for each main idea.

Language Proficiency Adaptation Accept short phrases or drawings for main ideas and details from beginning speakers. Encourage intermediate speakers, and require advanced speakers, to write in full sentences.

Main Ideas	Details

*Use the graphic organizer (GO13) in the **Transparencies** book to present this strategy.*

Spider Map

A spider map is a way to review and organize information that stems from a central topic.

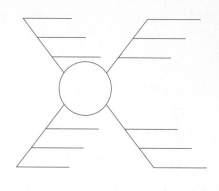

To create a spider map:

- Write the main topic in a circle.

- Draw diagonal lines branching off the topic and label these with the topic's key concepts.

- From the branches, draw horizontal lines that group facts, details, and examples to support each key concept.

Language Proficiency Adaptation Allow beginning speakers to work in small groups to complete their spider maps. Encourage intermediate speakers to work independently at first, and then share their work with another student, completing and revising their maps as necessary.

Use the graphic organizer (GO14) in the **Transparencies** *book to present this strategy.*

T-Chart

A T-Chart helps students organize lesson information including concepts, vocabulary, questions, and facts.

To create a T-Chart:

- Divide a sheet of paper into two columns. Write a heading for each column based on the information being organized. For example, you might use the headings Key Term and Definition.

- List information.

Language Proficiency Adaptation Provide beginning speakers with a partially completed chart. Make sure advanced speakers write in complete sentences.

Use the graphic organizer (GO15) in the **Transparencies** *book to present this strategy.*

Two-Column Table

A Two-Column Table is similar to a T-chart in that it organizes lesson information. It can also be modified to include additional columns as necessary.

Language Proficiency Adaptation Accept short phrases or drawings from beginning speakers. You may also wish to provide partially completed tables to beginning speakers. Encourage intermediate speakers, and require advanced speakers, to write in full sentences.

Use the graphic organizer (GO16) in the **Transparencies** *book to present this strategy.*

Venn Diagram

Students can use a Venn diagram to help them compare and contrast items.

To make a Venn diagram:

- Draw two (or more) overlapping circles.

- Write the unique characteristics for each topic in its own circle.

- In the center overlap, write characteristics that the topics share.

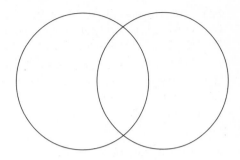

Language Proficiency Adaptation Provide banks of short phrases for beginning speakers to place in the diagram.

*Use the graphic organizer (GO18) in the **Transparencies** book to present this strategy.*

Comprehension Check Strategies

It is critical to check for student understanding as you proceed with a lesson. If you move forward and most of the class is not with you, you will lose the students. Each of the following strategies allows teachers to poll a class and see at a glance who is understanding a concept and who is not.

Card Responses Have each student prepare a set of cards, each card with one answer. Ask questions and have students hold up the appropriate card to indicate their answer to the question. For example, when studying habitats, students could create three cards, each with one of the following words: food, water, shelter. Ask questions describing each of these components of a habitat, and have students hold up the card appropriate for your description.

Signals Create a set of true-or-false statements or multiple choice questions with numbered answers to check student understanding of the material being taught.

- True-or-False: Make a statement and have students indicate with a thumbs up gesture if they agree or a thumbs down if they don't agree. Have students indicate their gestures in front of their chests to minimize others imitating their answers.

- Multiple Choice: Provide answers written on the board that are numbered 1–4. Ask questions for which one of the answers is appropriate. Ask students to hold up one, two, three, or four fingers to indicate which of the four answers is the correct one after each question.

Slates Have each student create an erasable slate by stapling a clear transparency to sturdy cardboard (staple a sheet of white paper between the two if a clearer writing surface is required). Provide students with erasable markers. Ask questions for which short answers are sufficient and have students provide answers by writing on their erasable slates and holding up their slates in front of them (three or four words should be the maximum length). Slates can be wiped clean with tissues to be used for subsequent questions.

Resources

References

Collier, V. & Thomas, W. (2002). *A National study of school effectiveness for language minority students' long-term academic achievement.* Santa Cruz, CA, and Washington, DC: Center for Research on Education, Diversity & Excellence. http://www.crede.org/research/llaa/1.1_es/html

Cummins, J. (1981). The role of primary language development in promoting educational success for language minority students. In *Schooling and Language Minority Students: A Theoretical Framework.* Sacramento, CA: California Department of Education.

Leos, K., (2004). *No Child Left Behind.* Paper presented at the annual conference of the National Association for Bilingual Education, Albuquerque, NM.

National Clearinghouse for English Language Acquisition (NCELA). (2008). *Educating English language learners: Building teacher capacity.* Washington, DC. http://www.ncela.gwu.edu/practice/mainstream/volume_I.pdf

National Clearinghouse for English Language Acquisition (NCELA). (2008). *How many school-aged limited English proficient (LEP) students are there in the U.S.?* Washington, DC. http://www.ncela.gwu.edu/expert/faq/01leps.html

National Education Association (NEA). (2008). *NEA 2008 Campaign Briefing Book.* Washington, DC. http://educationvotes.nea.org/userfiles/08%20CampaignBriefbk_bw.pdf

Science-Specific ELL Resources

Amaral, O., Garrison, L., & Klentschy, M. (2002). Helping English learners increase achievement through inquiry-based science instruction. *Bilingual Research Journal,* 26(2), 213–239.

Barton, M.L., & Jordan, D. (2001). *Teaching reading in science,* Alexandria, VA: ASCD.

Bernhardt, E. (1995) *Science Education and the Second Language Learner.* Columbus, OH: National Center for Science Teaching and Learning.

Calderón, M. (2007). *Teaching reading to English language learners, grades 6–12: A framework for improving achievement in the content areas.* Thousand Oaks, CA: Corwin Press.

Carr, J., Sexton, U., & Lagunoff, R. (2006). *Making science accessible to English language learners: A guidebook for teachers.* San Francisco: West Ed.

Colombo, M., & Furbush, D. (2008). *Teaching English language learners content and language in middle and secondary mainstream classrooms.* Thousand Oaks, CA: Sage Publications.

Dobb, F. (2004). *Essential elements of effective science instruction for English learners.* Los Angeles, CA: California Science Project. Available from http://csmp.ucop.edu/downloads/csp/essential_elements_2.pdf

Fathman, A., and Crowther, D. (Eds.). (2006). *Science for English language learners: K–12 classroom strategies.* Arlington, VA: NSTA Press

Jarrett, D. (1999). *The inclusive classroom: Teaching mathematics and science to English language learners.* Portland, OR: Northwest Regional Educational Laboratory. Available from http://www.nwrel.org/msec/images/resources/justgood/11.99.pdf

Lee, O. (2005). Science education and English language learners: Synthesis and research agenda. *Review of Educational Research,* 75(4), 491–530.

Medina-Jerez, W., Clark, D., Medina, A, & Ramirez-Marin, F. (2007). Science for ELLS: Rethinking Our Approach. *Science Teacher,* March 1, 2007, Arlington, VA: NSTA Press.

Rosebery, A., and Warren, B. (Eds.) (2008). *Teaching science to English language learners: Building on students' strengths.* Arlington, VA: NSTA Press.

Schleppegrell, M. (2002). Challenges of the science register for ESL students: Errors and meaning-making. *In Developing advanced literacy in first and second languages,* pp. 119–142. Mahway, NJ: Lawrence Erlbaum Press.

Siegel, H. (2002). Multiculturalism, universalism, and science education: In search of common ground. *Science Education,* 86, 803–820.

Professional Organizations

Teachers of English to Speakers of Other Languages: a global association for English language teaching professionals. The mission of this organization is to develop and maintain professional expertise in English language teaching and learning for speakers of other languages worldwide. http://www.tesol.org

World-Class Instructional Design and Assessment (WIDA): a consortium of states dedicated to the design and implementation of high standards and equitable educational opportunities for English language learners. http://www.wida.us

The U.S. Department of Education: the federal department that promotes educational excellence for all Americans. http://www.ed.gov

Office of English Language Acquisition, Language Enhancement, and Academic Achievement for Limited English Proficient Students (OELA): a division of the U.S. Department of Education whose mission is to help ensure that English language learners and immigrant students attain English proficiency and achieve academically. http://www.ed.gov/about/offices/list/oela

OELA's National Clearinghouse for English Language Acquisition & Language Instruction Educational Programs (NCELA): the division that collects, analyzes, synthesizes, and disseminates information about language instruction educational programs for English language learners and related programs. http://www.ncela.gwu.edu

Education Resources Information Center (ERIC): an online digital library of education research and information. ERIC is sponsored by the Institute of Education Sciences (IES) of the U.S. Department of Education. ERIC provides ready access to education literature to support the use of educational research and information to improve practice in learning, teaching, educational decision-making, and research. http://www.eric.ed.gov

Center for Applied Linguistics (CAL): a private, nonprofit organization working to improve communication through better understanding of language and culture. http://www.cal.org

Center for Research on the Educational Achievement and Teaching of English Language Learners (CREATE): a program of research designed to address specific challenges in the education of English language learners in the middle grades (Grades 4–8) http://www.cal.org/create

National Association of Bilingual Education (NABE): a professional organization whose mission is to advocate for the nation's bilingual and English language learners and families. NABE's mission also includes cultivating a multilingual multicultural society by supporting and promoting policy, programs, pedagogy, research, and professional development that yield academic success. http://www.nabe.org

International Reading Association (IRA): a professional organization whose mission is to promote reading by continuously advancing the quality of literacy instruction and research worldwide. http://www.reading.org

National Science Teachers' Association (NSTA): a professional organization whose mission is to promote excellence and innovation in science teaching and learning for all. http://www.nsta.org

National Council of Social Studies (NCSS): an association of over 25,000 educators whose mission is to provide leadership, service, and support for all social studies educators. http://www.socialstudies.org

National Council of Teachers of Mathematics (NCTM): a public voice of mathematics education, providing vision, leadership, and professional development to support teachers in ensuring equitable mathematics learning of the highest quality for all students. http://www.nctm.org